JOURNEY TO THE OTHER SIDE:

Talking to Angels and Other Benevolent Beings

Ted Mahr

Ted Mahr
1401 Marvin Rd NE, Suite 307
Box 231
Lacey, WA 98516
www.OutofThisWorld1150.com
OutofThis World1150@gmail.com
Outofthisworldradion@protonmail.com
1-888-879-8339

Publisher's Note: This is a work of fiction. Names, characters, places, and incidents are a product of the author's imagination. Locales and public names are sometimes used for atmospheric purposes. Any resemblance to actual people, living or dead, or to businesses, companies, events, institutions, or locales is completely coincidental.

Book design: Carolyn White/www.CarolynWhitePhD.com

Journey to the Other Side/Ted Mahr. -- 1st ed.

ISBN 979-8-363252044

Cover photo: © Ted Mahr. Taken on plane flight 2017 crossing the Pacific Ocean. See Chapter 1 for background

Acknowledgments:

My dear sweet Dad and Teri;

My Ancient Inca brother;

President John F. Kennedy and the First Lady Jacqueline Kennedy;

Professor Albert Einstein;

Nostradamus;

Mahatma Gandhi;

The Galactic Alliance;

Admiral Halisourus and the Pleiades

Adama, Zorra, and the people of Telos and the Hollow Earth;

Carolyn and Gerry White, Jill Tower, and Jan McCabe for all their wonderful help, advice, and encouragement!

Preface

Everyone has the ability to talk to spiritual beings on the other side of the veil. This ability can be easily learned with confidence, will, and a positive attitude; however, many lack confidence to develop these abilities. Like an athlete or a marathon runner, it takes practice, concentration, and effort – know you can do it!

The goal of this book is to give you the tools and confidence you need to talk with Angels and other benevolent beings on the other side as planet Earth shifts into the 5th Dimension.

My own spiritual journey started with Teri (my foster mother) in November 1994 when she read everything on my mind, and then answered all my questions before I had a chance to even ask them.

For nearly 20 years, she then taught me how communicate with Angels and other benevolent beings. Since then, I have been on a fantastic spiritual quest that has led me to communicate with Albert Einstein, President John F. Kennedy, Nostradamus, the Galactic Alliance, and many Angels and spirits on the other side.

I now regularly talk with benevolent Extraterrestrials, Angels, and other benevolent beings. As the Earth now shifts into the 5th Dimension, this book is meant as a guidebook to communicating with the other side and talking to these beautiful beings.

Each of us have at many Angels or spirit guides who can help us. They are all waiting to talk with you, so let us begin this beautiful spiritual journey to this wonderful New World!

Foreword

Ted Mahr is the reigning adviser of the esoteric and hidden world.

Every week he literally talks to Millions of people on his radio shows. And now, he has a book: "Journey to the other side: Talking to Angels and other Benevolent Beings."

This is a book that discusses shifting dimensions, guiding spirits, and, yes, your personal path into this world. Do you need any special training or protection for such travels?

Only one: an open heart... and a giving of Love.

~ James Redfield, *The Celestine Prophecy*

Planet Earth is Ascending!

Planet Earth is now rapidly ascending into the 5th Dimension. As the planet ascends, people will need to learn how to talk with Angels and other benevolent beings, so they can adjust and thrive in this beautiful new environment. This New Earth will include a level of abundance that has not existed on the old Earth.

The benefits of this new abundance will be great health, wealth, happiness, and a new planet based upon service to others (instead of service to self). With this new higher vibration on Earth will come the need to find, create, and attract real spiritual, financial, and personal wealth. Just as a rising tide lifts all boats, these higher vibrations help people raise their consciousness to create this new bounty. Thus, the goal of this book is help people learn and prosper in the higher dimensions, and in the words of John Lennon, help humanity ascend so we can all "live as one."

This Ascension process has really sped up since we have made the right choices. As a result, parts of the Earth will shift into the 4th and 5th Dimension by late 2022 - early 2025. One of the first places to experience the shift will be the Mt. Shasta area of Northern California, which in many ways is already in the 4th Dimension.

As President John F. Kennedy has told me many times, it is the destiny of planet Earth to become a peaceful, harmonious, and loving place. He says there is no reason for people to be in conflict or fighting, because we are all one – we all have the spark of the Supreme Being or God within us. When everyone realizes this, the entire planet will change for the better.

He tried to institute good changes here on the Earth when he was President in the early 1960s, but the changes he tried to implement were from the top down. He was assassinated before he could be fully successful. Nowadays the changes are coming from the bottom up from people like you and me, all working together to make this world a much better and happier place.

We are all souls inhabiting a physical body. We inhabit bodies to learn lessons in this Earth school, in order to ascend. We are all like students in different classes – some are young or new souls, just learning their soul lessons. Others are very old souls who have come back here to the planet to help humanity ascend. I myself have been here 52,000 years or approximately 720 lifetimes; this is my last lifetime here on planet Earth before

I ascend and return to my star family in the Pleiades. In fact, all of us on Earth have come from somewhere else, and many of us (like myself) have waited many thousands of years to help in the Ascension of humanity at this critically important time.

This book is meant to bridge the gap between 3rd Dimension and the higher dimensions. It is written to help people talk with their Angels and spirit guides on the other side. It is also an educational tool to help people understand and navigate their lives as we shift into the 4th and then 5th Dimension.

The advice and information you receive from benevolent spirits and Angels on the other side is never wrong, for the 5th Dimension is totally based on truth. Once you can access your Angels and spirit guides on the other side, nothing is impossible. With Angelic help, the impossible becomes possible.

CONTENTS

CONTENTS

PART ONE

INTRODUCTION

CHAPTER 1

TALKING TO ANGELS AND OTHER BENEVOLENT ENTITIES

I was very lucky to have my wonderful foster mother (Teri) who helped me develop my psychic abilities. Teri was a master psychic who helped police departments in the Seattle, Washington USA area find lost and missing children, and she was very good at what she did. However, she told me that it was, of course, at times depressing work because sometimes she would help locate children who had been murdered or abused.

For nearly 20 years, Teri taught me how to talk to the other side. Included in her teachings were life reviews where she helped me review every thought, act, and deed I did or have ever done. Typically, life reviews are usually only done when you pass on with the help of God, your Angels, and spirit guides. I was very fortunate to have that kind of daily life review. As a result of these daily life reviews, I have spiritually advanced nearly 500 lifetimes – at 80 Earth years per spiritual lifetime, I have advanced approximately 4000 years. This has allowed me to easily talk to the other side, and see into the past, present or future on this or other planets.

Life reviews are amazing! This is because you not only see, feel, and experience what you have done from your perspective, but also from the perspective of everyone (and everything, including animate and inanimate objects) who you have affected. If you call someone a bad name, you will not only experience what you have done from your perspective, but also from the other person's perspective. It can be a wonderful learning experience on what (and what not) to do.

Spirits who have passed on communicate with thoughts from the higher dimensions, so when you want to talk to either a relative or friend who has passed on, all you need to do is meditate and sit quietly. Then send love and light to the one you want to communicate with. Love is the most powerful force in the universe; it is also the currency of the higher dimensions.

Spirits from other dimensions are always around us. They show themselves in various ways. I have found one of the

easiest ways for them to show themselves is to come through in photographs, like in the picture below:

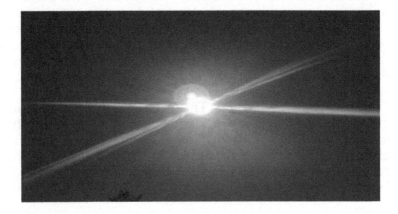

On the above picture, there is a red orb in the lower right-hand corner, and surrounding the sun are also multiple lighter reddish orbs.

As another example, this picture shows a cross of Angelic light from the sun, with an orb from the Pleiadians close to the sun:

As in the aboe picture, each orb represents a spirit, and since they are light bodies, it is sometimes easiest for them to come through photographs. Much of what you see in this picture is what I call "angel light", or the streaks of light from the sun. This is not just an optical illusion; it is actually Angelic light from the 5th and higher dimensions where these spirits live.

For example, when I was flying from Vancouver, Canada to Tokyo, Japan in April 2016, in the middle of the night 39,000 feet above the Pacific Ocean, I was given the message to photograph the moon. It was a beautiful moonlit night, and when I took the picture, a beautiful angel appeared:

The pink at either end of the picture is love (see cover photo.)

Angel over the Pacific Ocean

CHAPTER 2

LOVE IS THE LANGUAGE OF THE HIGHER DIMENSIONS

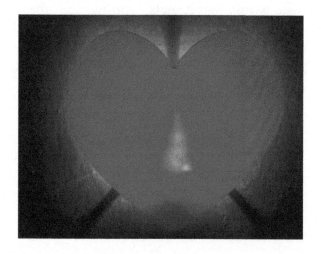

As Professor Albert Einstein has told me many times, the most important and powerful force in the universe is love; it is also the language of the higher dimensions. As Dr. Einstein writes:

"Love is Light that enlightens those who give and receive it. Love is gravity, because it makes some people feel attracted to others.

Love is power, because it multiplies the best we have, and allows humanity to not be extinguished in their blind selfishness. Love unfolds and reveals.

For love we live and die. Love is God and God is Love. "[1]

This force explains everything and gives meaning to life. It is the variable we have ignored for too long. It may be we are afraid of love as it is the only energy in the universe man has not learned to control at will.

If we want our species to survive; if we are to find meaning in life; if we want to save the world and every sentient being that inhabits it then love is the one and only answer.... (And) each individual carries within them a small but powerful generator of love whose energy is waiting to be released."[1] (Also refer to Chapter 27, Love is the Answer)

We all have loving guardian Angels around us, and spirits who want to help us. They all communicate through thought, so we have to pay particular attention to our thoughts and what messages we receive. This book will teach you how to communicate with our Angels, spirits, and the Ascended Masters. They are all here to help us, and they are waiting for you to talk to them. This book will teach you how.

---

1 https://suedreamwalker.wordpress.com/2015/04/15/a-letter-from-albert-einstein-to-his-daughter-about-the-universal-force-which-is-love/

CHAPTER 3

THOUGHTS ARE THINGS IN THE HIGHER DIMENSIONS

Thoughts are things in the 4th, 5th, and higher dimensions. We exist in the 3rd Dimension, but this dimension has a much lower vibration or frequency, so when you talk to Angels and spirits in the higher dimensions, they will often speak very rapidly because their frequency is so high.

When you receive messages from the other side, if they are benevolent, they will speak only truth to you. Spirits from the 5th and higher dimensions only present positive messages. Thus, the messages from these higher dimensions will always be uplifting.

In the 5th and higher dimensions, there is no such thing as "time" as we know it. When you talk to Angels and spirits in the 4th, 5th, and higher dimensions, all you will receive is the truth, and that truth can go anywhere in the past, anywhere in the present, and anywhere into the future on this or other planets, and galaxies and in other dimensions and realities. As Albert Einstein has written, "The distinction between past, present, and future is an illusion, although a persistent one."[1]

The only problem with looking into the future is that this is a planet of free will. When you look into the future, such views are always based upon what is happening now, and people's choices can always change the future based on their individual choices.

For example, Nostradamus once predicted that much of this planet would have been involved in a worldwide nuclear war by 2005, with many American cities in rubble.[2] There was a three-volume set of books written by Dolores Cannon from 1986 to 1989, in which she and about a dozen psychics traveled back to the 16th Century and spoke to him about his predictions. [3]

Nostradamus said that he wanted to speak to people in the 20th Century, because many of his predictions and quatrains were being misinterpreted – thus, he was happy to talk to Ms. Cannon and clarify his messages. In Dolores' books entitled *Conversations with Nostradamus* he laid out details of what he said would be an upcoming World War III.

However, since that time, I have spoken to Nostradamus. He has told me that the timelines have completely changed, so that there will now be no nuclear war and no Armageddon. When I first contacted Nostradamus in March 2015 for example, he was busy tearing up copies of the quatrains he had written about World War III.

When I psychically contacted him, he was sitting in front of a large oak desk, with a floppy red burgundy hat on in front of a fireplace. The date was December 1540, and the air in his room was smoky from the fire. After tearing up all these quatrains, he looked at me, and then asked, "What kind of world will you and your friends create?" I told him that I and many of my friends wanted to create a world of peace and harmony where conflict and war would be eliminated. He then said, "well, you better get busy" .... So since then, I have devoted myself to making this world a better place by raising consciousness.

The good news is, many of us here on planet Earth have made the right choices to make this world a much better place – and because of our good choices, Nostradamus says that there will now be no Third World War and no Armageddon. He and other great spirits say that all of us here on planet Earth have changed history. We now have a very bright and beautiful future ahead of us.[4] We still have many challenges, but I know we will continue to make the right choices and make this planet a peaceful and harmonious place.

1: Unsolved Mysteries of the Past, p.123

2 Conversations with Nostradamus by Dolores Cannon

3 Ibid.

4 Messages from the Masters, Ted Mahr

CHAPTER 4

THE NEW EARTH

The New Earth is coming rapidly and will be here before we know it, because majority of us on Earth have been making the right choices. According to Zorra and the people of the Hollow Earth, the rate of Ascension has sped up by six months to the point where parts of the planet will shift into the 5th Dimension by early 2025.

To give you a perspective on how quickly we are ascending, as previously mentioned, in the late 1980s, Dolores Cannon (a famous American psychic) and her students psychically contacted Nostradamus and with his help, gave detailed predictions of our future. As part of these predictions, humanity here on Earth was supposed to shift into the 5th Dimension by the year 2038.

However, by 2012, that timeline had been sped up to where humanity would shift into the 5th Dimension by 2028. Then by 2016, the timeline had moved up again to 2025. By this year (2022), the timeline has now sped up again where parts of the planet will shift into the 5th Dimension by early 2025 (or sooner). The shift will not happen all at once. Instead, certain already high vibrational parts of the Earth will shift into the 5th Dimension - one of the first places will be the Mt. Shasta area of Northern California.

Every year in early July and in late August/early September, I take a small group of people to visit Mt. Shasta. We meet with the high priest Adama and the people of Telos of the Hollow Earth. While there we do prayers and meditations at one of several entrances to Telos and the Hollow Earth. We have experienced what I call "miraculous healings" from Adama and others of the Hollow Earth. For example, while at Mt. Shasta in September 2018, the vision in both of my eyes was restored to perfect crystal clear 20/10 vision, from blurry 20/50 vision in my right eye. In September 2019, one lady who had had Lyme's disease for the past 20 years was spontaneously healed. Another man who had Lou Gehrig's disease was completely healed while visiting Mt. Shasta with my group in 2019. Another lady who had been crippled for 20+ years was given a new set of legs in September 2017.

According to my friends in the Hollow Earth, mother Earth (Gaia) has already started the Ascension process when the Schumann Resonance nearly doubled from 7.8 Hertz to 13.8 Hertz in September 2016 – since then, the frequency of the Earth has now exceeded 1000 Hertz at times and by 2022 - 2025, the frequency will increase up to 50,000 times what it is now and parts of the planet will shift into the 5th Dimension.

CHAPTER 5

THE BEST PLACES TO TALK TO ANGELS AND OTHER BENEVOLENT ENTITIES

To talk to the other side, the best, easiest way is to find a quiet place where you are relaxed and comfortable, preferably in a good positive mood. Often you can use nature and Gaia to help you communicate to the other side. Ley lines and positive energy vortexes are also excellent places to talk to the other side, because of the high energy and positive vibrations. For example, where I live in Olympia, WA there are several energy vortexes. There are others, at Mt. Shasta in California and Sedona in Arizona.

The entire area, from Mt. Shasta to Vancouver Island, was once part of Lemuria. When the Atlanteans destroyed much of the Earth 12,500 years ago, a large part of Lemuria broke off in the Pacific Ocean and drifted to what is now the west coast of North America. And the love energy of Lemuria and their beautiful civilization is still there along the west coast starting at Mt. Shasta and going north. You can feel it when you are there.

The energy is the reason so many psychics and spiritual people have relocated to the area. Of course, in other countries there are also many vortexes and positive energy ley lines. For example, the UK has vortexes and positive energy ley lines in Glastonbury and at Stonehenge. In Peru, the entire sacred valley from Cusco north to Machu Picchu is also filled with extremely high positive energy and ley lines.

This is not to say that you cannot talk to Angels and other benevolent entities from only these high energy places – you can contact Angels and spirits from anywhere on this planet. But some places have higher vibrations or are situated on ley lines, and so it is easier to make contact. There is a vast higher dimensional universe beyond this 3rd Dimension – this book will help you access this spiritual realm.

To access the other side, once you are comfortable, clear your mind of all thoughts. It is always good to protect yourself against all negative spirits and entities by covering yourself in a cone of white light and visualizing a series of mirrors facing outward to defect any negative entities or energies. Then ask spirit guides for this protection for from 12 to 24 hours. You could ask for longer, but the spirits always want people to work for spiritual protection and advancement. They are always happy to grant up to 24 hours of protection. As part of one's daily spiritual hygiene, I recommend that people protect themselves this way each day once a day, so they have continuous spiritual protection.

Spirits primarily communicate through thought. The physical aspects of the 5th Dimension are as real as that of our third dimension. The difference is when spirits talk with us, they use thought as the main way to communicate.

Since we are all light beings, it is relatively easy for spirits to appear as orbs, or streaks of light. Streaks of light are from the 4th, 5th, and higher dimensions.

The easiest way to see these orbs is to simply take a photograph – you see orbs appearing in the light. I have done this many times before. Each spirit has a particular color depending on their soul's purpose and spiritual development. I can always tell which entity is present. My wonderful and loving father, for example, is a reddish color, and my brother (Robert) is a blue orb. On the other hand, my sister (Lisa) is a greenish/yellow color, and my Aunt Sophie is a pure white. Red can be a very powerful color and it can radiate either love or hate. Blue indicates a spirit's soul purpose.

The colors of your aura or soul can designate your soul purpose. For example, the color of my aura is blue because I am interested in my soul purpose. My second color is violet, which means that I am interested in learning new and different things. White is the perfect color, closest to God (the prime creator); yellow is a very happy color and green is for healing. If you are a doctor or nurse, the color of your soul would likely be green.

Sometimes spirits will appear out of the corner of your eye. You will see them move across a room as a dark shadow, or in the form of an orb. Night vision goggles can help in seeing orbs, which are usually everywhere! Many times you will see nature spirits and fairies with these goggles.

Benevolent spirits often love singing and music and will congregate around someone who is playing beautiful music.

Often when you take a picture of the sun, you will see a spirit or a benevolent being as colored orbs in the photograph. For example, in the pictures below there is a reddish colored orb with another light orb in the middle.

The picture above was taken when I was at Mt. Shasta in September 2019. The reddish colored orb is from a Pleiadian commander. The other deep blue orb is one of my guides, "Jay He Nah," from Telos in the Hollow Earth. Streaks of light are what I call "Angelic light" from higher dimensions. As we ascend from this 3rd to the higher dimensions, we too evolve light bodies which are less dense and more ethereal.

Each of us has at least one guardian Angel around us, who helps protect us, and who provides spiritual guidance and moral support whenever we need it. Whenever you feel alone, or need guidance on any subject, please know that you are never alone, and that your guides are always around you. This book will help you contact your soul guides and spiritual family, as well as enable you to contact other benevolent extraterrestrial civilizations.

CHAPTER 6

THE 12 DIFFERENT DIMENSIONS

There are 12 different dimensions. We exist in the 3rd Dimension; Angels typically exist in the 5th and higher dimensions. Thoughts are things in the 5th Dimension. Because the 5th Dimension takes precedence over things in the 3rd Dimension, it is very important to keep your thoughts as positive as possible because they can control what happens in the 3rd Dimension. (See also discussion on the new 13th Dimension in Chapter 22)

There is no such thing as "death". When you pass over, you simply leave your physical body behind and make a transition to a higher and lighter dimension. Time exists as part of the 4th Dimension. However, in the 5th Dimension, there is no time as we know it here; there is no past, present, or future, because everything "exists in the now". A good psychic can go into the 5th Dimension, and see into the past, present, or future with great accuracy. A good psychic can also "remote view" scenes anywhere in the universe for any time period.

There is also no "quick fix" to gain access to benevolent spirits on the other side with mind altering drugs or alcohol. When you take drugs like marijuana or cocaine, you can get in touch with spirits on the other side, but these are often negative entities in the lower part of the 4th Dimension.

The nickname, "spirits" for alcohol actually has more than one meaning to Native Americans. Excess alcohol can be a gateway to the "spirit" world, but alcohol can create cracks in your aura's field, allowing negative entities to come into you.

As one example, negative entities will hang out at a bar waiting to enter people's auras who have drunk too much.

Spirits vibrate at a higher frequency than we in the 3rd Dimension. The easiest way for them to communicate is through thought. Often, when you want to communicate with a loved one on the other side, the easiest way is to send them a thought or a question like, "how are you?" And they will usually answer immediately.

The FIRST response you receive if immediate is usually the answer from them. When you start to communicate to the other side, you will often second guess yourself – but always follow your heart mind and your intuition. If the answer is clear, positive and immediate (before you can ask the question), the answer is from spirit. (Please see Chapter 7)

Spirits may also use an animal (like a bird or even a butterfly) to communicate with you. For example, let's say you are thinking of your wonderful Grandmother who passed on years ago. Suddenly, a bird comes to your window and stays there looking at you for hours. That is probably your grandmother telling you that she is with you, and she loves you! Butterflies and birds have a high vibration, so it is easy for a benevolent spirit to enter one of these beautiful loving creatures.

Another way spirits communicate is for them to perhaps give you the scent of their favorite perfume or cologne. There have been times when I have smelled the scent of my dad when he used to work out in the beautiful woods behind our farmhouse where I grew up in Olympia; whenever I would smell his "woodsy scent," I know he was with me, protecting and helping me!

Often when I am driving, I have several beams of what I call "angelic light" come through my window and surround my car completely! It is not sunlight; it is angelic light from the 5th Dimension, and when it happens, I am always so blessed because I know I am loved and protected by Angels and my spirit family. (See picture on next page)

Although my dad and my brother passed away some years ago, they will sometimes communicate with me through the telephone. Sometimes they will give complete sentences, and other times they may just give a word or two, like "you're right", or "good work". They are in the 5th Dimension, so they always speak very rapidly -- I have to write very fast to keep up with everything they are telling me.

CHAPTER 7

INFORMATION FROM BENEVOLENT ANGELS AND SPIRITS IS ALWAYS 100 PERCENT PURE TRUTH

For those of us used to the some of the information here in the 3rd Dimension as being sometimes false or misleading, the beauty of talking to benevolent spirits and Angels from the 5th and higher dimensions is that the information is almost always pure truth.

In the 5th and higher dimensions, everyone is connected to the Prime Creator who made all there is in this and other universes. Because it is pure truth, there is a clear transparency of thought in the 5th and higher dimensions that you seldom find here in the 3rd Dimension.

As Teri (my foster mother who taught me how to talk to the other side) would often say, when you try to hide your thoughts or lie to other people, it's like "running away from God". In the 5th Dimension it is impossible to lie since nothing can be hidden; it simply cannot be done.

When we all finally shift into the 5th Dimension in the next several years, the illusion of separation will disappear and absolute truth will be the way of things. As a result, many politicians and lawyers will find themselves out of work; people will instantly see through their lies and misstatements.

CHAPTER 8

THE "HEART MIND" OF THE 5TH DIMENSION VS. THE "LOGICAL MIND" OF THE 3RD DIMENSION

When contacting the other side, it's always important to be in a positive, upbeat mood, without any drugs or alcohol. Think of tuning into the other side as adjusting the dial on a radio or switching from channel to channel on a television set. If you take drugs or alcohol, the signal from the other side will become hazy and you will not be able to tune into any benevolent spirits. So, keeping your mind clear is very important and essential in talking to the other side. (Drugs and alcohol can lead you into the lower parts of the 4th Dimension where negative entities reside and can attach themselves to you.)

In the 5th and higher dimensions, thoughts are things. And as we ascend into the 4th and then 5th Dimensions, what you think about and what you wish for can and will materialize quickly. I myself live most of the time in the 5th Dimension and spend as little time as possible in the 3rd Dimension. In addition, in schools and throughout much of our lives we are also all taught to think "logically". However, as we move into the higher dimensions, the logic of the 3rd Dimension will give way to thinking with the logic of our heart mind of the 5th and higher dimensions.

Our heart mind is approximately 2000 times more powerful than our logical mind. Thus, the intuition of our heart mind is very powerful. It can be far more accurate than one's logical mind. In fact, "most people don't know this, but the heart can feel, think, and decide for itself. It has around 40,000 neurons and a whole network of neurotransmitters with very specific functions, which makes it a perfect extension of the brain" [1]

According to a Gaia television documentary, "Aristotle considered the heart as the center of reason, thought, and emotion, senior to the brain in importance. Ninth century Arabic philosopher Abu Nasr al-Farabi believed that, "The ruling organ in the human body is the heart; the brain is a secondary ruling organ subordinated to the heart."

Auguste Comte, a 19th century French philosopher declared that the brain should be servant to the heart. "The most common denominator in all religions is that the heart is the seat of wisdom," said Rollin McCraty Ph.D., director of research at the groundbreaking Heart Math Institute in Santa Cruz, CA. Twelfth century Christian mystic, Hildegard of Bingen, would agree. She wrote, "The soul sits at the center of the heart, as though in a house." [2]

So it is very important to pay attention to the messages you receive from your heart mind when talking to the other side.

---

[1] https://exploringyourmind.com/the-heart-has-neurons-too/

[2] https://www.gaia.com/article/mysteries-of-the-human-heart

CHAPTER 9

"DEATH" IS AN ILLUSION

My spirits and Angel friends on the other side tell me that there is no such thing as "death". Although your body does eventually cease to function here in the Third Dimension, we are all souls inhabiting a physical body, so when your body ceases to function, your soul will go on to the higher dimensions of the spirit world. When a psychic contacts spirits on the other side, they all say they are not "dead". They are simply living in another (higher) dimension. Once the energy of a soul is created, it cannot be destroyed. The soul will always exist. It is eternal.

It is getting easier and easier to contact the other side, because the vibrations of the Earth are now rapidly rising. These vibrations are also known as "global electromagnetic resonance phenomenon" or the "Schumann Resonance", named after physicist Winfried Otto Schumann who predicted it mathematically in 1952.[1]

For tens of thousands of years, the Earth vibrated at 7.8 Hertz. However, in September 2016, the vibration of this planet rose to 13.8 Hertz and has been rising ever since then. This year (2022) there are parts of planet Earth where the vibrations are now over 1000 Hertz. These vibrations should be many times higher than that by early 2025. With these high vibrations, parts of Earth will shift into the 5th Dimension by early 2025 or sooner.

According to Zorra and my friends in Telos of the Hollow Earth, Mother Earth has already shifted into the 5th Dimension. She is just now waiting for the rest of humanity to catch up and join her. All the planets in this solar system are shifting into the higher dimensions. The one planet waiting for so long for humanity to catch up and evolve is planet Earth. Of all the planets in this universe, the hardest one to effect any positive change has been Earth.

Evil was instituted as an experiment here on Earth with the hope that people would choose the positive path of life (over a negative one). But with the end of the Mayan calendar in December 2012, Prime Creator realized that evil as an experiment here on Earth had failed – she realized that it was time to end the experiment. The process has been slow, but we are finally now starting to evolve into the higher dimensions. It is finally time for humanity to evolve and ascend.

For those spirits who refuse to change, and who want to cling onto the old paradigm of negative thoughts and actions of the 3rd Dimension, there is a lower 3rd Dimensional sister Earth that has been created on the other side of this solar system. This sister Earth is in the same orbital path as this planet. For these negative souls, they will go to this negative planet on the other side of the solar system where they will be given one Mayan Katun cycle (or approximately 25,800 years) to work out their karma and make better choices. At the end of this cycle, they will be given the opportunity to ascend again if they want. However, for the rest of us, we will be ascending into the higher dimensions. Everyone is on their own spiritual path.

George Bush Sr. has gone to this other lower vibrational 3rd Dimensional Earth like planet, as has U.S. Senator John McCain. Once there, they will have one Mayan Katun cycle or approximately 25,800 years to ascend – I wish them well, and hope that they make better choices this time!

Many of us have waited a very long time for this to happen. I have been here on planet Earth for approximately 51,600 years or two Mayan Katun cycles. This is my last lifetime in 3rd Dimension on this planet. I would like to rejoin my star family from the Pleiades after my life is over here on planet Earth.

We are not all from this Earth – we came from somewhere else in this universe (or other universes).

---

1 https://en.Wikipedia.org/wiki/Schumann_resonances (See also discussion below in chapter 14)

CHAPTER 10

OUR GALACTIC HISTORY

We all came to this planet to help with the Ascension and be a part of it. Earth is a very special planet where we have free will, unlike other planets which do not have any free will. We started out from Lyra where we were an aquatic species, and then spread throughout the Universe. Today, the universe is teaming with life. Humans are a very common species throughout this Universe. Most people here on Earth came from the Pleiades, a 5th Dimensional civilization hundreds of light years from this planet. They are kind, benevolent beings who are helping us now with your Ascension.

There are 12 different dimensions, with God or the Supreme Being in the 12th Dimension. And at one time, we all had advanced to the 10th or 11th Dimension, right next to God in the 12th Dimension. But when we were in the 10th or 11th Dimension, many of us decided as a group to come down to the 3rd Dimension here on Earth to relearn all of our lessons; it was like going back to graduate school again and earning a PhD (or several PhDs). This is one of the reasons why we have such a wide range of emotions.

In addition, throughout the history of Earth, we have had at least 22 different ET civilizations visit us – sometimes altering our genetics to suit their own purposes. As a result of this, all humans on Earth are considered "genetic royalty" because we have the genetic strains of so many different civilizations encoded into our DNA.

This is one reason why our genetics are so highly valued by some negative species like the Reptilians and others, who view humans like cattle or chicken – a resource to be exploited and used for their own benefit. On a soul level, all of us are from somewhere else.

I myself am from the Pleiadians, a 5th Dimensional civilization that is approximately 444.2 light years from planet Earth[1] This is a star picture of the Pleiades, aka: "The Seven Sisters."

In November 2018, the homes of about 80,000 people in the cities of Paradise and Malibu, California were burned to the ground with particle beam weapons from the Reptilians and the Cabal controlled U.S. Air Force. After this a call was made by many light workers for help. I myself made a call out to the Galactic Alliance for help, because we were being hit with weapons in which we were completely defenseless. As a result, over 2 million Pleiadian ships responded and are now stationed around the planet – they will be here until planet Earth ascends. Many of the ships are drones. They have told me that they will not directly interfere, as they are here ready to help us – all we must do is to ask for their help as this is a free-will planet. They are all helping us with this Ascension. They are also making sure the planet does not have what is called a "pole shift", where one end flip flops on its end. For millions of years, one problem with Earth is that roughly every 100,000 years, the poles would flip, resulting in the destruction of most civilizations.   Humanity would then have to start over. However, this time, the pole shift will be prevented, so that we will all be able to shift into the 5th Dimension.

When I was at Mt. Shasta in July 2019, I met the Pleiadian Commander in charge of all their ships circling this planet – his name is Admiral Halisourus. Friends and I were at a campfire on Mt. Shasta one night – while there, we telepathically contacted this large Pleiadian ship above us. When we asked the ship to move right, it moved right; when we asked the ship to move left, it moved left. Then suddenly, we all saw an outline of Admiral Halisourus next to us at our campfire – he had beamed himself down to visit us! The Admiral was in the 5th Dimension while we were all in the 3rd Dimension. However, we could still see his faint outline in the light of the fire. We started talking to him; he said that his ships had been on their mission for the last six years. They would all be around planet Earth until we all had ascended. Since then, I have been in contact with Admiral Halisourus. He has provided invaluable assistance on many critical occasions.

1 https://www.gaia.com/article/who-are-the-pleiadians

CHAPTER 11

THE GALACTIC ALLIANCE AND THE REPTILIANS

There are two main Extraterrestrial Groups in this part of the Universe: (a) the Galactic Alliance and (b) the Reptilians. The Galactic Alliance is based on service to others, with harmony, peace, and love. The Reptilians are based on service to self, with tyranny, war, and hate.

Unfortunately, in March 1954, President Eisenhower entered into an agreement with the Reptilians. The agreement allowed the Reptilians to abduct and "study" humans, in exchange for some of their technology to fight the then Soviet Union. Unbeknownst to President Eisenhower, at the same time he entered into an agreement with the Reptilians in March 1954, the Soviets also entered into an agreement with the Reptilians. So they ended up playing both sides against each other.

The formal name of the Galactics is the "Galactic Alliance of Inter dimensional Free Worlds". They have approximately 450 million planets, with about 7 trillion entities. The Galactics are mostly (but not all) human, but they are all very benevolent and all care about us. They are here to help us in the Ascension process, and all are watching and assisting us. Their hope is that we will continue to make the right decisions to Ascension into the 5th Dimension. The Pleiadians are part of this alliance, as are the Arcturians, the Syrians, the Lyrans, the Andromedans, and other benevolent advanced ET human (and nonhuman) races.

As the planet shifts into the 5th Dimension, people will have more and more contact with our benevolent space brothers and sisters. Eventually, we will become a member of the Galactic Alliance. If President Kennedy had not been assassinated in 1963, we would have already shifted into the 5th Dimension. If President Kennedy had not been assassinated in 1963, we would all now have free energy. In addition, we would already be communicating telepathically, be much happier and healthier, and be living for hundreds of years.

CHAPTER 12

DR. MASARU EMOTO - WE CREATE OUR OWN REALITY

Because of our galactic history, we are all powerful spiritual beings who create our own reality. Therefore our (positive) thoughts are so important. Dr. Masaru Emoto was a famous Japanese scientist who discovered that our positive thoughts could create beautiful water crystals. He also discovered everything is Hado or vibration. As an alternative health doctor, he successfully treated about 10,000 people with special Hado or water vibrational machines for many different physical and spiritual illnesses, before he passed away in October 2014. He also created a beautiful children's project called the Emoto Peace Project where he taught children that love is the most important and powerful force in the universe. (See: www.emotopeaceproject.net) Dr. Emoto used to take pictures of frozen water crystals, with both positive and negative words written on bottles of water. The positive (or negative) words produced crystals; the words "love and gratitude" created the most beautiful water crystals:

Before he passed away, Dr. Emoto was on my Out of this
World Radio show from 3 pm to 4 pm PST on July 25, 2014 in
Bellevue/Seattle. Since 2013, I have a weekly spiritual and
metaphysical radio show, the purpose of which is to raise
consciousness and make this world a better place.

(See: www.outofthisworld1150.com)   I now broadcast on
BBS Radio in Texas on Saturdays and Mondays, and Radio Sol
International in Vienna Austria on Mondays – (See: https://
bbsradio.com/outofthisworldradio and www.radiosol.at) My
audience is over 250 million in over 100+ countries with
broadcasts in three or four different languages.

When I interviewed Dr. Emoto on my radio show, I asked
him if his meditation and prayer techniques could help bring
about world peace. He said yes that it should – so we did an
experiment where we sent lots of love and light to the
Palestinians and the Israelis who were fighting at the time in the
Gaza strip. We prayed and meditated for a 12 hour cease fire,
so they could exchange food and medical supplies.

After my radio show ended at 4 pm, I arrived at the place
where I was staying and turned on the TV at 8:30 pm. As soon
as I turned on the television, there was a little red banner across
the screen on CNN that said that the Israelis and the
Palestinians had just spontaneously agreed to a 12 hour cease
fire to exchange goods and medical supplies for the wounded
on both sides! I was happy, because our intention experiment
had worked! At the time, somewhere between 30,000 and
40,000 people were listening to the show and participating with
Dr. Emoto in this intention experiment for world peace. Now
my radio audience is over 250 million, and I think the lesson is
that we are powerful spiritual beings who can create our own
beautiful reality if we want! On January 3rd and January 10th,
2020 we also did another intention experiment and prayers for
rain for Australia on my radio show. The results were
outstanding, with much of Australia getting much needed rain
to help stop the fires across much of the country.[1]

---

1 http://outofthisworld1150.com/guests/intention-experiment-prayers-for-Australia/

CHAPTER 13

LEMURIA, MU, ATLANTIS AND EDGAR CAYCE

Like Dr. Emoto, the people of Mu, Lemuria, and Atlantis knew that all life was Hado or vibration – they were very advanced in their spirituality, raising their consciousness through individual and mass meditation. In fact, according to the famous American medical psychic Edgar Cayce, the people of Mu (an ancient civilization that predated Atlantis here on the Earth) excelled in spirituality, even surpassing the Atlanteans in psychic abilities.[1]

According to Frank Joseph, the soul practitioners of first Mu and then Atlantis engaged in mass-meditation sessions involving hundreds of thousands, and occasionally millions of participants"[2]. He writes that the "psychic power generated from these single-minded assemblies went beyond anything experienced before or since. Levitation of otherwise immovable objects, psychokinesis, communal telepathy, remote viewing, metaphysical healing, the shifting of space and time, prophecy, inter-species communication, inter-dimensional travel – the whole gamut of known psychic phenomena and far more than presently guessed were developed by the Lemurians and later refined by the Atlanteans." [3]

According to Edgar Cayce, the Atlanteans were expert at channeling spirits and astral projection. He writes, "through the concentration of the group-mind of the Children [Followers] of the Law of One, they entered into a fourth-dimensional consciousness – or were absent from the body"[4] (Edgar Cayce, Atlantis)

According to Frank Joseph, the "Atlanteans had psychokinesis – the ability to influence physical objects by thought processes – literally down to a science ..."[5] He writes, "the coordinated mental exertion of perhaps thousands of persons, disciplined and working together at the same moment, generated unimaginatively powerful psychic energy."[6]

---

1 Frank Joseph, Atlantis and the Coming Ice Age, Bear and Co.: Vermont. c.2015

2 Ibid., p.152

3 Op. Cit., P.152

4 the Edgar Cayce Readings. Vol.22, 2464-2 F. 24, c.1987, quoted in: Frank Joseph, Atlantis and the Coming Ice Age, Ibid., p. 153.

5 Frank Joseph, Atlantis and the Coming Ice Age, p. 153

6 Ibid., p.153

CHAPTER 14

THE SCHUMANN RESONANCE-THE RISING VIBRATIONS OF THE PLANET EARTH

The Earth is slated for ascension into the higher dimensions, and as of September 2016, the planet shifted into positive energy for the first time in at least 26,000 years. For thousands of years, the Schumann resonance or the vibration of the planet was at 7.83 Hz. Then on January 31, 2017, for the first time in recorded history, the Schumann resonance reached frequencies of 36+ Hz.[1]

As of May 8th, 2017, the frequency of the planet has now spiked to up to 120 Hertz![2]   And since then, the frequency of planet Earth has now exceeded 1000 Hertz in many areas![3,4]

Why is this happening now?   Gaia or Mother Earth has decided that she has waited long enough for humanity to ascend, so she has now started to shift into the higher dimensions. By the summer of 2025, parts of Mother Earth will be in the 5th Dimension. Mt. Shasta in Northern California will be one of the first places to shift into these higher dimensions.

As time goes by, with the rising Schumann frequencies, it will be easier and easier for people on the surface of the planet to physically meet and talk to the people of Telos of the Hollow Earth. As we raise our frequencies, we will in fact be able to meet Adama (the high priest of Telos) and the people of Telos and the Hollow Earth as we will be much closer in terms of vibrations or frequencies to their high vibrations.

Because everything is "Hado" or vibration, with the rising vibrations and frequencies of the Earth, we are now shifting into the higher dimensions. We will soon be able to freely talk to the other side, and to other benevolent Extraterrestrial civilizations, in addition to the people of Telos and the Hollow Earth.

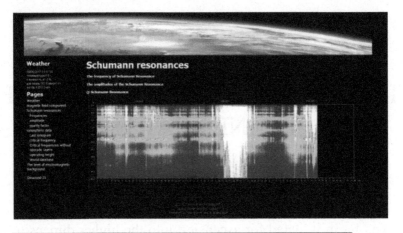

1 http://www.drjoedispenza.com/blog/consciousness/what-does-the-spike-in-the-schumann-resonance-mean/

2 http://whispersfromthesoul.com/2017/05/schumann-resonance-spikes-may-8th-110-120-hertz/

3 https://www.disclosurenews.it/en/schumann-resonance-today-update/

4 https://www.heartmath.org/gci/gcms/live-data/gcms-magnetometer/

CHAPTER 15

EFFECTS OF THE NEW HIGHER VIBRATIONS

Physical Effects

As the Schumann Resonance continues to rise on our way to the 5th Dimension, many of us will find ourselves increasingly tired (even when we get a good night's sleep). Please do not be alarmed, because when we feel tired, it just means that our body is adjusting to these new, higher vibrations. When you feel tired, be sure to get some extra rest – there is nothing wrong with you. Your body is only adjusting to the new vibrations. Most of us in human form on this planet have evolved for tens of thousands of years on the old frequency of 7.8 Hertz. However, with vibrations exceeding 1000 Hertz in many parts of the planet, all our bodies are now needing some additional time to adjust to the new frequencies.

The second thing these new vibrations are doing is that they are awakening the dormant DNA within cells. Many Earth scientists mistakenly call these additional strands in our DNA to be "junk DNA", implying that they are not needed. "At least 75 per cent of our DNA really is useless junk after all."[1]

In genetics, the term "Junk DNA" refers to regions of DNA that are noncoding" and assumes that because they do not create proteins in the cell, this so called "Junk DNA" is not needed.[2]

However, we are powerful spiritual beings, and this junk DNA is supposed to help us in this ascension process to the 5th Dimension. As we adjust to these new higher frequencies, this so called "junk DNA" will be activated, allowing of us to communicate telepathically in one language, and help all of us adjust to the 5th Dimension (see discussion below).

Spiritual Effects

As the vibrations rise and the Earth shifts into the 5th Dimension, negative beings will not be allowed to live here anymore. Mother Earth is tired of being abused by negative people. Some say she has already shifted into the 5th Dimension. People must be at least 51 percent of service to others, and they will then ascend. If not, they will go to another lower 3rd Dimensional Earth like planet on the other side of this solar system in the same orbital path as this planet. It will be a sister planet to Earth where souls will be given one Mayan Katun cycle (or 25,800 years – or the time it takes to revolve around the Central Galactic Sun) to ascend. The journey never ends – we are all going back to Source or God or the Supreme Being (the entity who created all of this).

However, even with positive people, some may experience some negative periods in their lives because if they have any negativity within them that needs to be purged, this negativity will come out. If this happens to you, please just release any negativity within you -- take responsibility for your choices in the past and then release them. Forgive and love yourself as much as possible. The negativity will have to be purged to ascend into the higher dimensions.

The Supreme Being, or God, or Source has decided that Earth will ascend. There is nothing that the negative entities can do to stop it. During this ascension process, it will be important to be strong and to never give up. And if someone attacks you with negativity, do not react immediately, but please try instead to send them lots of love and light. I realize that this might be difficult to do, but when you react with negativity to someone who has sent negativity to you, you are only lowering your vibration by sending negativity back to them. As Mahatma Gandhi said, "An eye for an eye only ends up making the whole world blind."[3]

My spirit guides also tell me that everyone will be tested by their higher self, but at the same time, all challenges are meant to be solved. To cope with these changes, just accept and allow them to happen and it will be a smoother ride. Also, do not be in fear, and do not be influenced too much by the mass media, which feeds off fear. Often what passes for "news" is disinformation. The truth for one may not be the truth for another. This brings up another point -- during this ascension, respect other's truth, but you don't have to agree with it, because everyone is on a different soul path. On the other hand, anything not in alignment with the higher beings will cease to exist.

With the higher vibrations and the shift into the 5th Dimension, colors will become much more vibrant. Reds, for example, will become more vibrant, blues more intense, greens much deeper, etc. With the higher vibrations, people will live much longer – hundreds of years longer. On planets with advanced benevolent human societies, the average longevity of most humans is about 1000 years, with some living as long as 25,000 years. And as we advance into the 5th Dimension, we will also easily live to 300, 400 years and longer.

Communications

We will all communicate telepathically in the New Earth. People today communicate through oral and written language in the 3rd Dimension. However, many misunderstandings can occur among people when they do not understand each other's words, oral or written. However, when the planet shifts into the higher dimensions, many people will communicate telepathically. This is a form of pure communication in which people will be able to instantly read each other's minds without any distortion. When this happens, it will be impossible for anyone to hide anything from anyone else and everything will be totally transparent. For those trying to commit crimes or steal or cheat, what they are thinking and doing will be evident to everyone concerned.

As we ascend into the 5th Dimension, we will all be able to communicate telepathically. With this will come the important knowledge of Unity Consciousness – that we are all one, with the spark of the Creator, or God or the Supreme Being within all of us.

The Tower of Babel was real.⁴

At one time, we also communicated with one language. In this sense, the Tower of Babel in the Bible was real (see: Genesis 11:1-9). According to the New Revised Standard Version:

"Now the whole earth had one language(telepathy) and the same words. And as they migrated from the east, they came upon a plain in the land of Shinar and settled there. And they said to one another, "Come, let us make bricks, and burn them thoroughly." And they had brick for stone, and bitumen for mortar.

Then they said, "Come, let us build ourselves a city, and a tower with its top in the heavens, and let us make a name for ourselves; otherwise, we shall be scattered abroad upon the face of the whole earth." The LORD came down to see the city and the tower, which mortals had built. And the LORD said, "Look, they are one people, and they have all one language; and this is only the beginning of what they will do; nothing that they propose to do will now be impossible for them.

Come, let us go down, and confuse their language there, so that they will not understand one another's speech." So the LORD scattered them abroad from there over the face of all the earth, and they left off building the city. Therefore, it was called Babel, because there the LORD confused the language of all the earth; and from there the LORD scattered them abroad over the face of all the earth."⁵ The "LORD" referred to in the above paragraphs were nothing more than not so benevolent

Extraterrestrials who transformed the one language we spoke at one time here on the Earth into many different languages where we could not understand each other.

This splitting of our original one language into many languages allowed the "LORD" (read "ETs") to control us – it is easier to control humanity when we are split into many cultures with many languages and cannot talk to each other. However, this oneness that once existed here on Earth will reappear with the universal planet wide ability to communicate with telepathy.

---

1 New Scientist, 2017 – see: https://www.newscientist.com/article/2140926-at-least-75-per-cent-of-our-dna-really-is-useless-junk-after-all/#ixzz67f2707Iz

2 Medical Life Sciences News, February 26, 2019 -- https://www.news-medical.net/life-sciences/What-is-Junk-DNA.aspx

3 https://www.brainyquote.com/quotes/mahatma_gandhi_107039

4 http://www.ldolphin.org/babel.html "The Tower of Babel and the Confusion of Languages"

5 https://global.oup.com/obso/focus/focus_on_towerbabel/

CHAPTER 16

THOUGHTS

Thoughts are very important in the 5th and higher Dimensions. Thoughts are things in the 5th Dimension. And when you communicate with your Angels, spirit guides, and benevolent Extraterrestrial entities in the higher dimensions, nearly all communication is done with your thoughts. So, it is very important to pay attention to what you are thinking and the messages you receive, because the main way Angels and spirits on the other side communicate is through thought. The physical attributes of the 5th Dimension are just as real as those of this 3rd Dimension. However, it is different in the sense that when spirits communicate with us in this 3rd Dimension, they use thought as the main way to communicate.

Spirits in the 5th Dimension may also communicate through animals, butterflies, birds, clouds, and other objects. The vibration rate of a butterfly is much higher than of us humans, so it is easy for a higher vibrational spirit to join with a butterfly and come to see you. I have had instances where a butterfly will land on my hand and stay there for some time, before flying off. Usually, the butterfly is from my dad or other guardian Angels, letting me know that they love me and are thinking of me. Another way a spirit can communicate is to materialize a penny, usually face up (Abraham Lincoln penny in the U.S.) in front of you, in what I call a "penny from heaven." (See Chapter 25.) Other ways spirits appear is through light, especially during sunsets, where orbs of light will appear. The easiest way to see these orbs is to simply take a photograph, and you will see the orbs appearing in the light. (See Chapter 1.)

CHAPTER 17

ANGELS

We are all surrounded by Angels. Each of us has at least one guardian Angel around us, who helps protect us, and provides spiritual guidance and moral support whenever you need it. Whenever you feel lonely, or in need of guidance on any subject, please know that you are never alone. Your guides are always around you from the instant you enter your mother's womb until you finally pass over.

As a suggestion, I would take a picture of a relative who loves you and who is now on the other side and meditate as you look at his or her picture. Make sure that your pineal gland is free of fluoride (see chapter 23), and you are in a positive, upbeat mood, preferably in nature.

Cover yourself with a cone of white light, followed by a series of mirrors facing outside (or blue flames), and ask God and the Angels to protect you for 24 hours. When that 24-hour period has ended, then I would ask God and the Angels to protect you for an additional 24 hours, so you repeat this every day as part of your spiritual hygiene. I would then thank the higher spirits for their protection and follow this with chanting the sound "Hu" three, four or five times to bring in the benevolent Galactic Alliance for help and protection.

If you feel that you are being bombarded with a lot of negativities, you might also imagine covering yourself with 12 inches (or more) of a thick lead shield, and ask Archangel Michael to come and protect you.

CHAPTER 18

THE IMPORTANCE OF KEEPING A JOURNAL

Only after you have employed some of these protective measures would I attempt to contact the other side, and/or benevolent beings from off this planet. Thoughts are things on the other side, so it is very important to pay attention to your thoughts. I always recommend that my clients get a journal and write down the questions you want to ask the other side, and then make contact.

Before you can complete your question, the answer will be in the back of your mind. If the answer is not instantaneous then it's your ego and not spirit. Do not second guess yourself. Trust is a must! Record your answers in your journal.

Since there is no time on the other side, the spirit you contact knows your question before you ask it. They give you the courtesy of starting the question before they provide you with the answer. The answers are correct when talking to the Angels and other benevolent beings. Accept the communication and don't "over think" the answers -- this can lead to "analysis paralysis."

The Angels and spirits on the other side always communicate very rapidly since they live at a much higher vibration or frequency than we here in the 3rd Dimension. So when you talk to the other side, messages often will come in very fast, and you have to get used to the fast frequency or pace of the other side. Start with questions which require one- or two-word answers.

Once you start writing in your journal, you can review it in the future for messages from the other side for guidance and advice – and the advice from the other side is very often more valuable than gold. If possible, it is also good to have a psychic mentor who can double check your answers. It can be a slow process at first, but after a while I guarantee that you will be able to easily talk to Angels and many benevolent spirits on the other side, including Extraterrestrials. Like swimming or riding a bike, it just takes practice and the will, love, and determination to do it, and you will be successful.

As you get tuned to talking to your guides and Angels, they will send you messages, sometimes during the day when you are awake. And sometimes at night you will receive messages when you are asleep in a dream state. So, it's very important to write down your thoughts and keep those channels open. It is not an easy process, but you can do it, and the rewards will be great! When you write down spirit messages, they usually come to you very rapidly. So you must grasp their messages very quickly. The messages come to you very fast from the 4th and 5th Dimensions, and you must write very fast to capture the messages.

The spirit world is vast place, much larger than our own 3rd Dimensional reality here on Earth. If you would like more detailed information, there is a book called the Urantia Book that gives an overview of Angels and the Angelic world.[1]

Everything I said here about writing down messages from Angels also applies fully to your dreams. When you first wake up in the morning, it would be a good idea to write down any dreams. Dreams are just as real as this 3rd Dimensional reality – they are just from the higher dimensions where your loved ones, who have passed, are living. Even though a dream may not make any sense when you write it down, often a dream will be part of a larger message in which the meaning will become more important later. Remember, thoughts are things in the 5th and higher Dimensions, so it is always a good idea to pay attention to your dreams and your thoughts, and to write them down (if possible).

---

1 https://www.urantia.org/inspiring-questions/did-humans-evolve-or-were-they-created

CHAPTER 19

TIME/ASTRAL TRAVEL

With love and determination, you can also time travel or astral travel. When clairvoyance is used to view events in the past, present, or future on this planet or in other dimensions, the process is called "remote viewing". The physical part of the body used for remote viewing is the Pineal Gland.

Time or astral travel are best accomplished when in a good mood, and in a comfortable position. Many people find it helpful to be in nature when you do this, because the beautiful energies of Gaia can spiritually help you when you contact the other side. Then with your eyes closed, visualize two copies of yourself just outside of you. Then project one copy of yourself to whenever you want, past, present, or future, or anywhere on this planet, or elsewhere in the Universe. Once you have projected yourself to another location in another time, you can talk to the people or entities there. When you have finished your visit, close the session by asking God or the Supreme Being to return the copy of yourself back to you. Once back, merge the first copy with the second copy of yourself and merge the copies into yourself. With practice, you can travel anywhere in the Universe and visit with anyone and/or observe any event, past, present, or future on this or on other planets.

Examples:

I have time traveled to see my dad before he passed away. I miss my dad – he passed away in March 1999. When I was a young man, we used to go fishing at a local lake near our farm. With these techniques, I can time/astral travel back to where we used to go fishing and enjoy a very happy and wonderful time with him! And I can do it at any time I like (if he is not busy and is available to come with me on a one of our wonderful fishing trips)!

You can also use these same techniques to remote view and view the assassination of the beloved U.S. President, John F. Kennedy on November 22nd. 1963. Using these techniques, you can find out the truth for yourself on who really killed President Kennedy. With these methods, you can see that Lee Harvey Oswald did not shoot President Kennedy.

Instead, there were triangulation shots fired from three different locations by three different groups of gunmen: (a) a US Army sharp shooter from a manhole about 25 yards in front of JFK's limousine, (b) from the grassy knoll about 40 or 50 yards from his vehicle by two Mafia sharp shooters, and finally (c) from another close building by a team of three marksmen from the CIA. [1]

You can also remote view how Vice President Lyndon Johnson ordered the U.S. State Department to send out a pre-written, canned press release on how Lee Harvey Oswald killed President Kennedy on November 22nd, 1963 (the day that JFK was killed). You can also view how this was sent out on November 21st to all U.S. Embassies around the world (with instructions to release it on November 22nd).

The only problem with this press release is that in Auckland, New Zealand, when it was November 22nd, the date in the U.S. was November 21st. When the U.S. Embassy dutifully issued Johnson's press release on November 22nd in New Zealand, the problem was that JFK was still very much ALIVE in the U.S. So it was a little embarrassing for New Zealand newspapers to publish the news of JFK's murder when he was still alive – see front page of the Christchurch newspaper on JFK's assassination. Back then, communications were not as quick as they are today – the entire episode was buried very deep by the Johnson Administration and the U.S. controlled media.[2]

(See discussion in my book, *Messages from the Masters*, pp. 27-29 and the copy of a 1963 newspaper article in Appendix B.)

In 1992 on a flight from Seattle to Tokyo on Northwest Airlines, I was watching a movie. It was a long flight, and while seeing the movie, I fell asleep. I dreamed of some future scenes in the movie. When I woke up, the movie was still on, but then I saw the scenes which I had just dreamed about.

This illustrates an important lesson – when you dream, you often go into the 5th Dimension (where there is no time), enabling you to time travel into the past, present, or future. So, when I was sleeping in the 5th Dimension, there was no time, enabling me to literally see into the future.

---

1 Cf.Lebedev, Treason for My Daily Bread, Part 4, 1077.

2 https://christchurchcitylibraries.com/Heritage/Newspapers/Star23Nov1963/output/thumbnails/Thumbs1.asp

CHAPTER 20

THE "NEW" HUMAN OF THE 5TH DIMENSION

When you enter the 5th Dimension, time traveling and/or remote viewing any event or place in the past, present, or future will become very easy. There is no "time" as we know it in the 5th Dimension, so when you enter the 5th Dimension, you can easily go anywhere into the past, present, or future on this or other planets in this Galaxy or Universe. We are very powerful spiritual beings. We have capabilities we do not realize that we have.

In our DNA for example, there are 22 strains of what our Earth scientists call "junk DNA". However, they are far from "junk". These DNA strains were shut down by the Annunaki when they changed our DNA to create good workers to mine gold for their planet, Nibiru, many thousands of years ago.

However, with the rising vibrations of Earth, we are all waking up and these strains of so called "junk DNA" are now being activated. Once these DNA strains are fully awake, we will realize our full potential and become the powerful spiritual beings which we are meant to be. This will include telepathy for everyone, and the ability to heal ourselves easily. There will be no more disease on planet Earth because there will be no more "dis-ease", People will learn to live harmoniously and in peace – as we were meant to be.

CHAPTER 21

OUR SEVEN CHAKRAS WILL SOON GO TO EIGHT

All of us have seven different chakras, which represents one's life force. "In a healthy, balanced person, the 7 chakras provide the right balance of energy to every part of your body, mind, and spirit. If one of your chakras spins too quickly, slowly or is blocked your health can suffer.[1]

In the etheric body, the chakras "are rotating energy-centers" and "their task is to take energy from the cosmos into your being and send it to the spot in you where it's needed."[2] In Sanskrit, chakra means "wheel" or "disc" and "our chakras serve as receivers, transformers and distributors of Prana (or Chi) the Universal Life Force."

The continuous rotation of the chakras causes energy to be processed and released in a never-ending energy exchange with the cosmos. Without this energy there is no physical existence. If there is one or more of your chakras not functioning properly - meaning it either absorb or release too much energy can lead imbalance with the remaining chakras. This disharmony between the chakras can be (and often IS) the source or the reason for mental and physical illness.

At present in this 3rd Dimension, the seven major body chakras are:

1. The Root Chakra
2. The Sacral Chakra
3. The Solar Plexus Chakra
4. The Heart Chakra

5. The Throat Chakra
6. The 3rd Eye Chakra, and
7. The Crown Chakra.

According to one source,[3]

"The first chakra relates to survival, strength and basic 'being', it's position near the rectum, at the end of the spinal cord. The first chakras color is a fiery red and connected to the red ray.

The second chakra relates to emotions, creativity and sexuality, our 'basic needs' so to speak. It's positioned at genital-height and its color is orange and therefore associated to the orange ray.

The third chakra is the chakra of will-power and metabolic energies. It is positioned at the Plexus Solaris (Near stomach). The color of the third chakra is yellow, connected to the yellow ray of light.

The fourth chakra is our Heart-chakra. And you might've guessed it's position: Near the heart. It's therefore connected with love and feelings. The color of the Heart-chakra is Green and of course associated with the green ray.

The fifth chakra is the chakra of communication and fine-tuned creativity. It's positioned near the throat. Its color is a turquoise blue. The fifth chakra is associated with the blue ray.

The sixth chakra is connected to clairvoyance, meditation, intuition, and spirituality in general. This chakra is also called "The Third Eye" and is positioned on your forehead, right between your physical eyes. The color and ray associated with the sixth chakra is indigo.

The seventh chakra is connected to knowledge and insights. It is the last chakra to be literally connected with our physical bodies. The color of this chakra is violet." – The colors of the chakras are like the colors of a prism or a rainbow.

And when all these colors and chakras are turning in perfect harmony, a bright white light is formed which is the Eighth Chakra. According to one source, "this chakra that has been forgotten in so many writings about auras and chakras is the last step of your physical, 3D, body.

Chakra 8 is positioned a little above your head and is diamond shaped. This chakra is also called the "Throne of the Soul" It's through this chakra that we connect with our Higher Selves to receive guidance and Light. It's the "portal" to our 4th and 5th dimensional bodies."[4,5]

And as we shift into the 4th and then 5th Dimension, this new Diamond shaped 8th Chakra will appear above our crown chakra.

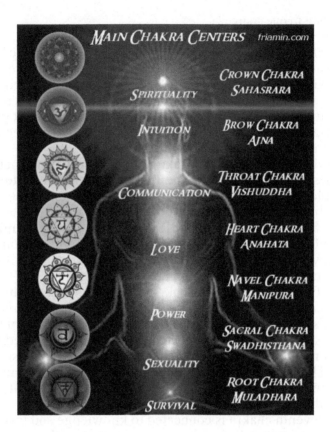

1 https://blog.mindvalley.com/7-chakras/

2 http://accnl.tripod.com/chakras.html

3 http://accnl.tripod.com/chakras.html

4 http://accnl.tripod.com/chakras.html

5 See also where people talk about the 8th chakra of Krishna : https://www.speakingtree.in/allslides/krishna-the-

THE NEW 13TH DIMENSION

When we start shifting into the 5th Dimension here on Earth, all other dimensions will also shift one dimension higher, and a new 13th Dimension will be created. This new 13th Dimension will all be part of the Ascension not only for Earth, but for all the other planets in this solar system, as well as the rest of the Milky Way Galaxy.

Currently, there are 12 Dimensions, with the 12th Dimension as the home of God or the Supreme Being (the entity who created all that is). At present, we exist in the 3rd Dimension but as we shift into the 4th and then 5th Dimensions, all the other dimensions will also shift one dimension higher.

According to Zorra of the Hollow Earth, the 5th Dimensional civilization of Telos and the Hollow Earth beneath Mt. Shasta will shift into the 6th Dimension, and the Supreme Being will shift from the 12th Dimension to this new 13th Dimension.

This is an exciting, historic time for all of us now on Earth. All eyes from every part of this universe are now watching us to see how we progress and ascend into the 4th and then 5th Dimension. Our Ascension is literally the greatest show in this Universe. All of us on Earth have chosen to be here to be part of this historic moment!

With this new Dimension, people here on Earth will also be experiencing a new diamond shaped chakra that will float right above their crown chakra. This new crown chakra started appearing several years ago and is now very pronounced in many people. Dr. Carolyn White, PhD has researched this topic and taken many pictures of this new Diamond shaped chakra.[1]

The following picture shows the location of this new Diamond-shaped, or Star chakra, located above the crown chakra.[2]

1 interview on BBS Radio on my Out of this World Radio Show for Monday, August 15th, 2022 at: https://bbsradio.com/outofthisworldradio or www.outofthisworld1150.com under "Past Guests" or "Podcasts

2 www.justtheessentials.ca

PART TWO

TALKING TO THE OTHER SIDE

CHAPTER 23

PREPARATION – HOW TO PROTECT YOURSELF WHEN TALKING TO THE OTHER SIDE

1. ALWAYS COVER YOURSELF WITH WHITE LIGHT AND ASK FOR ANGELIC PROTECTION

Thoughts are things on the other side. So it is very important to be in a positive frame of mind whenever you attempt to contact the other side. Like attracts like so you want to only attract positive, benevolent spirits and Angels to talk to you.

However, because there are negative entities, it is also always a good idea to protect yourself when you contact the spirit world. Whenever you contact the other side, always cover yourself with a cone of white light and a shield of mirrors facing outward to protect yourself against any negativity. I recommend that you ask for protection for 24 hours, and then renew it every day. You can ask for more time, but the Angels usually want you to work for the protection, so they will usually give you only 24 hours of protection. I call this "spiritual hygiene". Like brushing your teeth or showering, it's something that you should do every day. I have been told that the famous American psychic, Deloris Cannon, would cover herself and her clients using the same techniques before doing readings. She would however visualize a pyramid of white light for both herself and her client.

Also, if you want extra protection, you can also imagine a 12 inch (or more) lead shield around yourself, and/or ask Archangel Michael to guard you with his sword. Archangel Michael is a warrior spirit who protects and helps people.

Everyone has guardian Angels around them. Often once your family and relatives pass over to the other side, they join with your guardian Angels, and you can contact them for advice and guidance. Other times you can ask for specific Angels to come in and help, protect, and guide you. There are hundreds of Angels, but one of my favorites is Archangel Michael.

The guardian Angel of Mt. Shasta in Northern California is St. Germain. He is a wonderful and benevolent ascended master who will help you – all you need to do is to ask. While at Mt. Shasta in September 2017, the violet flame of St. Germain visited me and others at one of the entrances to Telos and the Hollow Earth while on Mt. Shasta:

One beautiful prayer to St. Germain states in part as follows:

"Mighty I Am Presence, Divine Healing Source, The All That Is,
The I AM That I AM:
I (We) Envision Beloved Earth and All Life upon Her to be Raised
in Frequency and Vibration to the Highest Level possible at this
time.

I (We) ask for Your Divine Powers to assist the planet and myself
(ourselves) in the Manifestation of this Vision and Desire ...

I (We) ask the Violet Flame to Transmute, within All Humans on
Earth, all negativity, undue control, greed, corruption, egotism,
poverty, disease, anger, hate and fear, as much as the Law will al-
low and in respect to the free will of all ...

Violet Flame, please transmute all that no longer serves me (us) -
body, mind and spirit. Turn that energy into the frequency of my
(our) Higher Self, allowing me (us) to step into that aspect of myself
(ourselves)." [1]

Another Angel who can assist you is Saint Francis. If you
like, you can say this beautiful prayer to him before contacting
the other side if you like:

'The Prayer of Saint Francis:
Lord, make me an instrument of thy peace.
Where there is hatred, let me sow love;
Where there is injury, pardon;
Where there is doubt, faith;
Where there is despair, hope;
Where there is darkness, light;
Where there is sadness, joy.
O divine Master, grant that I may not so much seek

To be consoled as to console,

To be understood as to understand,

To be loved, as to love;

For it is in giving that we receive;

It is in pardoning that we are pardoned;

It is in dying that we are born to eternal life." [2]

Another beautiful prayer which you can also say before contacting the other side is from Buddha:

> *"May all beings be filled with joy and peace.*
> *May all beings everywhere,*
> *The strong and the weak,*
> *The great and the small,*
> *The mean and the powerful,*
> *The short and the long,*
> *The subtle and the gross:*
>
> *May all beings everywhere,*
> *Seen and unseen,*
> *Dwelling far off or nearby,*
> *Being or waiting to become:*
> *May all be filled with lasting joy.*
>
> *Let no one deceive another*
> *Let no one anywhere despise another.*
> *Let no one, out of anger or resentment,*
> *Wish suffering on anyone at all.*
>
> *Just as a mother with her own life*
> *Protects her child, her only child, from harm,*
> *So within yourself let grow*
> *A boundless love for all creatures. "spirits in rocks"*
>
> *Let your love flow outward through the universe,*
> *To its height, its depth, its broad extent.*
> *A limitless love, without hatred or enmity.*
>
> *Then, as you stand or walk,*
> *Sit or lie down.*
> *As long as you with a one-pointed mind;*
> *Your life will bring heaven to earth."* [3]

In addition, for creativity, you can ask Archangel Uriel for help in finding a solution to any problem or issue.

These protections really do work -- I urge you to employ them if needed. There is a vast spiritual universe out there full of many benevolent Angels and spirits who very much want to help and guide you. ⁴

2. ALWAYS DO THE "HU" AND ASK THE GALACTIC ALLIANCE FOR HELP AND PROTECTION

Another protection you can do is to sing the word "Hu" from the Galactic Alliance. The universe is teaming with life. There are good and bad spirits and Extraterrestrial entities, and good and bad groups. One of the good groups is called the "Galactic Alliance" made up of 450 million planets, with about 7 trillion entities. They are mostly human, and are all benevolent and want to help us. To ask for their protection, just sing the word "Hu" (as in human) three or four times, and they will come in to protect and help you. The Galactic Alliance is between 50,000 and 100,000 years ahead of us technologically, and between 30,000 and 50,000 years ahead of us spiritually. To call on the Galactic Alliance for help and protection, always sing the "Hu". The "Hu" is derived from the word "Human". When you sing the "Hu", it will also open up your pineal gland and expand your consciousness for help with any problem or issue. I usually sing the "Hu" three or four times after I have covered myself with white light and mirrors.

We are all very powerful spiritual beings. In fact, we are all "Gods" and "Goddesses", with the spark of Source or the Supreme Being or God all within us. We are all amazing beings, with the ability to heal ourselves and perform miracles. With practice and dedication, we can also go into other dimensions and contact Angels and benevolent spirits, as well as Extraterrestrial life beyond this planet.

If you do not protect yourself, you can pick up negative entities which can influence and/or control you. So I always recommend that people use protection when they contact the other side.

Many times children, teenagers and young adults will play with a Ouija board. They think it's fun but usually have no idea that negative entities can come in and easily attach to them. Once a person has a negative entity or spirit attach to them, it can be difficult to rid yourself of their negative influences. If you do have a negative attachment, always do the "Hu"

meditation and ask the Galactic Alliance to help rid you of their
negative influences.

3. A HIGH VIBRATION DIET WITHOUT MEAT, AND DRINKING WATER WITHOUT FLUORIDE ARE IMPORTANT

To become more spiritual, it's good to have a high vibrational
diet, one without meat. When the animals are killed and you eat
their meat, the fear they experience when they were killed goes
into the meat and your vibrations are lowered. Those who eat
meat have a particular energy signature. If you visit Mt. Shasta,
the people of Telos and the Hollow Earth are able to sense that
signature. So whenever you visit Mt. Shasta and want to go into
the Hollow Earth, it's a good idea to stop eating meat at least
three weeks before your visit. If you do eat meat, it is a good
idea to bless the meat by suspending your hands over the food
and blessing the animal for giving their lives, so you can sustain
yours.

If you live in an area with fluoridated drinking water, your
pineal gland is probably calcified and blocked. So it is a good
idea to first get the fluoride out of your body, and then to drink
fluoride free drinking water. Fluoride is a neurotoxin that is a
poison and blocks your intuition and psychic abilities.[5]

Although fluoride was marketed in the U.S. as a way for
people to reduce cavities after World War II, few people know
the real story of how fluoride in our water was started in the
United States. Shortly after World War II, some in the U.S.
Government wanted German Nazi scientists and engineers to
help rebuild the U.S. economy.

So during the years after World War II, "Operation Paper
clip" was started where nearly 10,000 Nazi scientists and
engineers were brought to the United States to work in
government and in the U.S Military Industrial Complex. These
Nazi scientists urged the U.S. Government to fluoridate water
supplies, based upon what Adolf Hitler had done in Germany
during the 1930s and 1940s in the Nazi concentration camps.
After the Reptilians signed a formal agreement with the Nazis
in 1936 for cooperation and assistance, they urged the Germans
to fluoridate the water supplies in their concentration camps

(which they did). When concentration camp inmates drank this fluoridated water, they became docile, obedient workers who did not question authority – the perfect workers for a tyrannical dictator. Over time, the fluoridation of water completely ossifies your pineal gland, so you do not have any intuition or psychic abilities. Over a long period of time, fluoridated water causes cancer and decreases the IQ of most people. Some U.S. Government officials really liked this idea and so today, 70 percent of all municipal water supplies in the United States are fluoridated. In England, all municipal water supplies are fluoridated.

If you live in a city that has fluoridated water, I strongly recommend that you buy the best water filter you can buy to filter out the fluoride from your drinking and bathing water. Second, I recommend that you buy a bottle of "Arctic Skate Liver Oil". Arctic Skate Liver Oil is the only known substance in the world which will completely remove all the fluoridate out of your pineal gland and the remainder of your body.

Fluoride is officially classified as a neurotoxin (see above). It is clearly not beneficial in any way. If you are learning to contact the other side, I strongly recommend that you filter your drinking water and take some Arctic Skate Liver Oil – one table per day will remove all the fluoride from your pineal gland and body within two weeks. A bottle of 120 capsules is inexpensive and will last you about four months.

Interestingly today, no cities in Germany fluoridate their drinking water supplies because they know what it does to people and that it originally came from Adolf Hitler.

4. ALWAYS REMAIN IN A GOOD POSITIVE MOOD, FREE OF BOTH DRUGS AND ALCOHOL

To prepare for psychic contact with the other side, always remain in a positive mood. Spirits and Angels find it much easier to contact you when you are in a positive frame of mind. In addition, because like attracts like and "birds of a feather flock together", it is always good to be in positive mood because you will attract other positive Angels and other positive entities.

It is also always a good idea to always have a clear mind free of any drugs or alcohol. There is no "short cut" to gaining access to the other side with drugs or alcohol. Some people have told me that I should use marijuana to "quickly" gain access to the other side. Marijuana will get you to the other side, but it will only bring you to the lower parts of the 4th Dimension where many negative entities live. Drugs and/ alcohol can create holes in your aura that will allow negative entities to enter your energy field – this of course, can cause many problems.

5. ALWAYS GROUND YOURSELF AS MUCH AS POSSIBLE AND IN NATURE

Mother Earth or Gaia will always help you contact the other side by assisting you to "ground" yourself. This can be done by simply walking barefoot on a lawn, or along a beach or a forest – anything that will put you in contact with Mother Earth. Another way is to drive through a nature park or a beautiful natural area -- the natural energy of Gaia will help ground you. In contrast, some say living in an apartment, condo, or office several floors above the ground can actually cause mental illness because they lose contact with Mother Earth. This condition can be remedied by spending more time in nature. As the famous American Naturalist, John Muir has said, "the clearest way into the universe is through a forest wilderness." [6]

6. ALWAYS GET RID OF ANY NEGATIVE IMPLANTS

When contacting the other side, you should rid yourself of any negative implants you may have. I am happy to help people get rid of their negative implants, or you can get rid of them on your own. How we all got implanted is a long story. Everyone on this planet has been infected by negative implants, thanks to an agreement entered into by President Dwight D. Eisenhower in March 1954, with negative Extraterrestrials called the "Reptilians", a negative group of tyrannical ETs who helped the Nazis during World War II.

Eisenhower was threatened by these Reptilians into signing an agreement with them. The 1954 agreement specified that in exchange for some of their advanced technology to fight the Russians during the cold war, they would be allowed to "abduct" and "study" us humans. As a result of that illegal agreement, everyone on this planet has been infected with "negative implants" which cause people to be negative. This illegal agreement is called the "Treaty of Merida" (which was never ratified or authorized by Congress and has been kept secret since 1954). This agreement was important to the Reptilians who feed off of negative energy generated by war and other types of conflict. Basic human nature is to be positive, loving, and service to each other. The Reptilians had to implant negativity in humans to achieve service to self.

There are two levels of negative implants: (I) negative surface implants and (II) deeper negative soul implants. Thanks to this illegal 1954 agreement with the Reptilians, all humanity was infested with negative surface and soul implants. To remove the negative surface implants, all you need to do is to say is, "5, 4, 3, 2, 1, With the God (if you are a man) or Goddess (if you are a woman) in me, I now own and control all negative implants within me, and nothing or no one can negatively affect or control me. I know this to be true."

This statement will disable any negative implants within you and allow you to more easily contact the other side in quiet meditation. With respect to the deeper soul implants, if you chant the mantra, "huuuuuuuuuu" several times a day, and ask the Galactics, they will remove your negative soul implants.

Earth is a planet of free will and so you have to ask for help from the benevolent ETs. The Law of Free Will states that no entity whether human, ET or spirit being may directly affect another entity without their permission, to do so incurs Karma. The negative ETs like the Reptilians (and their allies, the Greys) do whatever they want without regard to the Law of Free Will and view humans as a food source to be exploited and used. One can only imagine the amount of negative Karma they have accumulated for themselves.

7. SAGE, SEA SALT, AND THE USE OF 528 HERTZ TUNING FORKS

To further prepare to talk to the other side, it always a good idea to clean your area, so there is no negative energy. To clean an area, you can use sage, sea salt, and 528 Hertz tuning forks.

Sage has been used by many Native North Americans to clear negativity from areas. Good spirits love burning sage – they will stay when you burn sage, but negative entities cannot be in the same area when sage is burned. So when you want to clear negative energy, just burn some sage.

It is always a good idea to sprinkle some sea salt in every corner of each room – this will also help clean out negative energy and drive away any negative spirits.

The frequency of unconditional love is 528 Hertz, so when you strike a tuning fork tuned to that frequency, you project love everywhere. I often use 528 Hertz tuning forks to help clear areas, and it really works!

---

1 https://ascension-stgermain.com/prayer-earth.html)

2 Eknath Easwaran, Meditation. Nilgiri Press: Tomales, CA. c.1991. p. 220

3 Ibid. -- Eknath Easwaran, Meditation. pp.221-222

3 For a list visit http://www.archangels-and-angels.com

5 "Fluoride As a Neurotoxin: 9 Ways It Harms Your Brain", Be Brain Fit, c.2018, at: https://bebrainfit.com/fluoride-neurotoxin/

6 http://www.globalstewards.org/spiritual-faith-god-quotes.htm

CHAPTER 24

PRACTICAL EXERCISES

Once you have prepared to contact the other side, there are many different exercises which you can use to contact Angels and other benevolent beings. Please note – there is no fast or easy way to contact the other side. You can't use drugs or alcohol to speed up the process or contact the benevolent spirits or Angels. When you use drugs or alcohol, you do go to the other side, but you go to the negative lower part of the 4th Dimension where negative entities reside. Once in the lower part of the 4th Dimension, these negative entities can and will attach to you – they can make you act in negative ways.

Benevolent spirits and Angels will use thoughts to communicate with you; thoughts are objects in the 5th and higher dimensions. It is important to pay close attention to your thoughts when you contact the benevolent spirits. In addition, like attracts like. So, to attract positive spirits, it is important to maintain a positive, uplifting mood. The law of Attraction is real, like does attract like, so maintain a positive mood when talking to the other side.

People use various tools to contact Angels and Benevolent spirits including pendulums, Tarot cards, tea leaves. These methods all work on the same principal, using intuition and what I call "heart mind". Louie Armstrong was right when he recorded his song, "It's a wonderful world". The universe really is a friendly place. Sometimes it's hard to see that when you are dealing with negativity in the 3rd Dimension, but remember the light reveals that hidden by the dark, and the best way to change the world is to start with yourself. As Mahatma Gandhi once said, "Be the change you wish to see in the world."

When you contact benevolent spirits and Angels on the other side, surround yourself with white light and mirrors to deflect any negativity. Chant the "Hu" mantra which will bring in the benevolent Galactic Alliance to help guide and protect you. It's important to keep a journal of the questions and answers you receive from the other side and look back at them from time to time or when needed for reflection. Often they will give you profound and important messages so keep them for future reference.

Deception does not exist in the 5th and higher Dimensions, there is only truth. So when you receive messages from Angel and other benevolent spirits, you will receive the true answers to all your questions. This of course is very different from the 3rd Dimension where people will sometimes not tell you the truth, but the new Earth of the 5th Dimension will be one based 100 percent on truth. When I was first learning how to talk to the other side over 20 years ago, I sometimes tried to second guess the answers I received from benevolent spirits. But when I did that, it was always incorrect. I learned long ago to trust the answers I receive.

When you ask questions of the other side, accept the first answer you receive if that answer is instantaneous. Don't second guess the answers you receive. When you talk to the other side, it's important to concentrate, and quiet your mind, because a busy mind will not hear messages from the other side.

As we move up the dimensional ladder from 3rd Dimension to the 4th, 5th, and higher dimensions, we become more and more light bodies. This is why spirits in the higher dimensions often will come through as orbs and streaks of light, as explained earlier (See Chapters 1 and 5).

1. THE IMPORTANCE OF MEDITATION

Before you start your day, it is always a good idea to take some time (15 to 20 minutes) to meditate. Start by covering yourself with white light, and mirrors and asking the Galactic Alliance for help (as explained above). Once you have taken these protections, first try to clear your mind of any thoughts, and then ask your spirit family to come in and help you.

As Lao Tzu has wisely said, when you pray or meditate to talk to the other side,

"Empty yourself of everything.
Let the mind rest at peace.
The ten thousand things rise and fall while the Self watches their
return.
They grow and flourish and then return to the source.
Returning to the source is stillness, which is the way of nature." [1]

Once you have cleared your mind, you can contact spirits. All of us have many spirit guides, part of our spiritual family who will help us. They typically are parents, grandparents, relatives, and friends who have passed on.

In addition, you can ask for help and protection from God, Jesus, Buddha, and other ascended masters, and/or Angelic protection from Angels like Archangel Michael or many others. This will allow and enable you to talk to the other side through your heart mind.

In October 2019, I spent a week at a meditation retreat with a wonderful group called the BK Kumaris. [2] They have a meditation retreat center at Mt. Abu in western India, where people meditate every day and attend spiritual classes. They are wonderful people and I really enjoyed being there. They would meditate for perhaps several hours or longer, with beautiful serene music first thing in the morning starting at 4:30 am.

The experience transformed my life and really helped me sharpen my meditation skills and ability to contact the other side. It is always a good idea to take some time during a busy day to meditate and get the answers you seek from within.

The BK Kumaris also have a hospital at Mt. Abu where they play music for a few minutes every hour – everyone is encouraged to meditate when the music plays. They say that the meditation helps everyone be happier, and work better. The hospital is called the "Global Research Hospital" and it is one of the best hospitals in India. [3]

2. VISUALIZATION

Visualization can also as an aide to contact the other side. For example, you can visualize objects or places on the Earth to help you go to the other side. As one example, you can visualize a skyscraper with 12 floors, with each floor corresponding to the 12 different dimensions. Using this visualization, you can start on the 3rd floor (corresponding to the 3rd Dimension) and then imagine walking into the elevator and getting off on the 5th floor into the 5th Dimension.

To help in this visualization, you can practice counting down. This can be done by simply saying "5, 4, 3, 2, 1, I am now stepping out of the elevator and into the 5th Dimension!" You can use this same count down technique to go to other dimensions.

When you get off the elevator into the 5th Dimension, the colors are far more intense (and more vibrant) than they are here in the 3rd Dimension, because the vibrations are much higher. Thus, the blues are bluer, the reds are redder, the yellows are yellower, and the greens are much greener. When you get off the elevator into the 5th Dimension, there is a transparency of thought not found in the 3rd Dimension where everyone can read each others minds with clarity and spoken language becomes secondary. Each of the 12 different dimensions of this Universe has physicality but each is different. As you move from lower dimensions to higher dimensions, you become closer and closer to the Supreme Being, or God (the entity who created all of this). The common thread for ascension is that you also get closer and closer to the light, with light being God. Before he passed away in 2014, one of the world's most famous spiritual people, Dr. Masaru Emoto, said that "God is water, and Water is God".

I have been visiting the Mt. Shasta area of California since 2015. When I first visited Mt. Shasta in August 2015, I was taken to the City of Telos by Adama and the people of the Hollow Earth. Both men and women wore long white robes, with men sporting long beards. They look just like us on the surface, but are generally a little taller and stockier. Their civilization is 5th Dimensional, and they communicate telepathically, with language being used secondarily. They are all very loving and benevolent. The City of Telos is set on a hillside about 100 miles beneath Mt. Shasta inside the Earth.

They have sunlight from an artificial sun, which produces golden light. Interestingly, their sunlight does not produce any shadows.

There are several portals to Telos and the Hollow Earth on Mt. Shasta. Anytime I wish to visit Telos and the Hollow Earth on the astral plane, all I need do is simply visualize these portals and I am taken into the Hollow Earth. If you have visited a sacred plane in another dimension, you can also use this same technique to travel to any other dimensions, on this or other planets.

Adama is the beautiful guardian spirit of the City of Telos underneath Mt. Shasta. I contact him and my guardian Angel from Telos, a wonderful lady named "Jay-Hee-Nah". Jay-Hee-Nah has a beautiful deep blue spirit that comes to me whenever I am at Mt. Shasta – see picture below:

When Dolores Cannon gave me a reading in 1996, she first hypnotized me and then led me to a beautiful flower meadow on the slopes on Mt. Rainier in Washington State. During that three hour reading, she brought me back to an ancient life time as a poet and philosopher in Greece in 3000 BC, and then 100 years into the future to the year 2096 were I was an engineer on a Pleiadian craft circling high above the Earth. I will never forget what I saw from the ship – a beautiful deep blue and peaceful Earth in the 5th Dimension. The Earth and its inhabitants were in complete peace and harmony; there were no more wars or conflict. Paradise on Earth had finally been achieved.

Now whenever I want to go back to that reading and visit ancient Greece or fly above the Earth in an advanced Pleiadian craft, I only need to visualize that beautiful flower filled meadow on the slopes of Mt. Rainier, which then will lead me to these other dimensions and realities. Once you have connected with your past, present, or future using this kind of powerful visualization method, you can use it anytime you like to revisit any places you previously visited on this or other planets.

When I visit Mt. Shasta, I have the most amazing experiences! In July 2019, I was with several people around a campfire. We were all looking up at the stars when I saw this Pleiadian craft – it was rectangular shaped with six lights. I have nearly 30 years of experience in talking to the other side, so I started sending lots of love and light to them, along with other people in my group. Then as an experiment, I asked the ship to go left (and it did). Then I asked it to go right (and it did). And finally after a series of these movements, the commander of the ship beamed himself down to the campsite where we were camping and we could all see him simmering in the campfire light in the 5th Dimension. He said his name was Pleiadian Admiral Halisourus; he was in charge of the 2 million Pleiadian ships now circling the Earth. Everyone had lots of questions for him. He said that his group will be here circling the Earth until humanity ascends to the 5th Dimension. He said they are here to help us, and it is up to us to make the right choices for ascension. They all respect the "prime directive" where each species on each planet is entitled to their free will choice of evolution. They said this evolution (and our free will choices) have been interfered with by the Reptilians, but that they cannot help us unless we ask for help. So I encourage everyone reading this now to please ask the Pleiadians for their assistance. Thanks to this experience, whenever I wish to contact Admiral Halisourus, all I need do is visualize his image around that campfire and his ship, and I can talk to him (as long as he is available and not too busy).

3. THE USE OF PENDULUMS, TAROT CARDS, AND OTHER AIDS

(a) Pendulums

I myself use a pendulum to sometimes double check the answers I receive from the other side. Using a pendulum is very easy. You first cover yourself with a cone of white light and mirrors for protection, and simply hold it steady and then ask your questions. For me a "yes" answer is when the pendulum swings back and forth to and from you. A "no" answer is when the pendulum swings back and forth left to right (or right to left). A clockwise circular motion indicates that the answer is uncertain, and a counterclockwise circular motion indicates that the spirits will not tell you the answer. When you first use a pendulum you should test to see how your pendulum moves for 'yes', 'no' etc. Ask the pendulum "show me 'yes'", "show me 'no'" etc. When used properly, a pendulum can provide extremely accurate answers to almost any question. However, questions always need to be asked in a narrative, "yes" or "no" format.

(b) Tarot cards

In like fashion, Tarot cards can be extremely useful in obtaining detailed, helpful answers to nearly any spiritual question. They were first created in the late 14th Century when artists in Europe created the first playing cards, which were used for games. By the 18th Century, people began to assign specific spiritual meanings to each card.

Today, there are hundreds of different Tarot decks available, but each deck "consists of 78 cards. The first 22 cards are the Major Arcana. These cards have symbolic meanings focused on the material world, the intuitive mind, the realm of change. The remaining 56 cards are the Minor Arcana and are divided into four groups or suits: Swords, Pentacles (or Coins), Wands and Cups. Each of the four suits focuses on a theme. Sword cards generally indicate conflict or moral issues, while Cups reflect matters of emotion and relationships. Coins focus on the material aspects of life, such as security and finance, while Wands represent things like jobs, ambition, and activity."[4]

Many tarot readers believe that the future is fluid, so when they interpret tarot card layouts, they focus on the possible outcomes for the person receiving the reading. Tarot readings are intended to give people information, so they may make more informed choices. A Tarot reading consists of dealing cards out in what is called a spread.

There are many different ways to use a deck of Tarot cards. One way is to shuffle the deck of Tarot cards, ask your question then pick a card and read the card that reflect matters of emotion and applies to you, or doing what is called a spread of cards after you have spiritually cleansed and shuffled them. Before using any deck of Tarot cards, you should always take the cards in your right hand (if you are right handed), and hit them hard into the palm of your left hand – this will clean out all the energy out of the cards before you use them. If you are left handed, you simply take the cards in your left hand and then hit them hard into the palm of your right hand before you use them.

Two of the most common Tarot card spreads are the Three Fates and the Celtic Cross. Each card represents a different perspective. For example, the Three Fates is a spread of three cards. The first card is the past; the second card is the present; and the third is the future. Other spreads cover other topics such as the current situation or obstacles and advice to overcome the obstacles; or what the person can change or cannot change for the situation.

The "Celtic Cross" spread is a spread of ten cards, which can be used to answer almost any question on any topic, as illustrated below: [5]

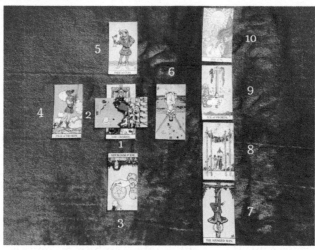

The "Celtic Cross" card spread can reveal the spiritual reasons, the challenge, the past, as well as the future of almost any topic.[6] Of the many available Tarot card decks, one of my favorites is the "Angel Card Deck" by Doreen Virtue and Radleigh Valentine.[7] There are many other excellent Tarot card decks, and you should use the one that resonates with you. Using Tarot cards is a highly intuitive process that takes some practice – as with many other things, practice does make perfect when learning how to use Tarot cards.

(c) Dowsing Rods

Like Pendulums, dowsing rods are much more than they appear, because they can connect you in the 3rd dimension with Angels and your guides in the higher dimensions, and help you obtain any answer on any topic you like!

Dowsers are usually two rods witch cross each other for a "yes" answer, and swing across each other for a negative answer. Like a pendulum, they move with how the Angels and guides direct them. Using dowsers can provide excellent and accurate answers to almost any question. But, as with any technique, you still need to prepare and protect yourself before using any dowsers to find answers to your spiritual questions.

There are of course other aids such as palmistry, astrology, and other methods for contacting the other side. All are valid if they resonate with you and are useful and helpful.

---

1 Lao Tzu – from: http://www.globalstewards.org/spiritual-faith-god-quotes.htm

2 https://www.brahmakumaris.org/

3 http://www.ghrc-abu.com/home

4 https://www.learnreligions.com/tarot-basic-overview-2562790

5 https://www.learnreligions.com/tarot-cards-how-tarot-readings-work-95948

6 Doreen Virtue and Radleight Valentine, Angel Tarot Cards, Hay House, Inc. c.2012

7 Ibid

CHAPTER 25

MESSAGES FROM HEAVEN

The Pineal Gland is essential to communicate and receive messages from Heaven.

The pineal gland is an amazing organ with the same eye cells found in your eyes. However, the eye cells in your pineal gland are very important because they connect with God and your intuition.

According to one source, "the pineal gland is a cone-shaped brain structure the size of a rice grain. It produces a variety of neurochemicals, most notably the feel-good chemical serotonin and the sleeping hormone melatonin. Humans have praised the pineal gland for thousands of years. The Egyptian Eye of Horus represented power, protection, and good health. Not to mention that it closely resembles its shape. Even earlier, 5,000-year-old Ayurvedic texts called it the third eye chakra (Ajna in Sanskrit)".

The pineal gland is considered the doorway to a higher dimension. It's the structure responsible for humans seeing beyond everyday linear reality. Intentionally activating your pineal gland (or third eye) tunes you into a reality beyond the five senses.

Pineal Gland - Third Eye

In other words, it's the connection between physical matter and immaterial energy (sometimes called the quantum).

Your third eye exposes the interconnectedness of life. Put practically, it's essentially your sixth sense. Your intuitive self, that perceives things before they occur. Scientifically, when stimulated it produces some fascinating mind-altering molecules. Unfortunately, fluoride blocks the Pineal gland making it impossible to tie into God to use your intuition. In addition, the so-called vaccines used for Covid also wipes out the pineal gland, as well as all the other chakras. This results in people becoming biological robots where they have no emotions and can feel no love or compassion. They essentially become biological entities without any feelings.

The Galactics tell me that people who take the vaccines now will lose all of their emotions and become the Greys. This is because the mRNA technology introduces Grey and Reptilian DNA into a person's cells, so they are no longer human. And some people who take the vaccines will eventually become like the Greys – biological entities without love, compassion, or any feelings. The Galactics also tell me that there is a race of beings called the "Sessoni" who are part Greys and part human. At one time, the Sessoni were human, but took vaccines like the ones being pushed today by many governments, so they were not human anymore. However, the Sessoni decided that they wanted to become human again, so they are now slowly evolving back to humans, with the help of the Galactics and the Pleiadians. It is very important to remove any fluoride out of your body if you want to talk to Angels and the other side. The best way to clean the fluoride out of your body is to take Arctic Skate Liver Oil every day for two weeks, and then to drink only filtered water without any fluoride. If you have taken the vaxx and destroyed your pineal gland, there are remedies available in Appendix A of this book.

If you live in an area where the water is fluoridated, demand your government to stop fluoridating your drinking water. Fluoride is a poison that does nothing but harm your body and shut down your pineal gland you so become a walking zombie without any intuition or connection to God.

Angels and spirits often will give you messages and talk to you through dreams. They will also sometimes talk to you through what is termed, "clairaudience". Or you may see things through what is called, "clairvoyance" with your pineal gland or "Third Eye". Angels and spirits can also communicate through animals, insects, clouds, stones and crystals, as well as other objects (including pennies).

The following is a list of ways spirits and Angels can communicate with you:

1. PENNIES

Spirits sometimes will send you a message by materializing a penny in front of you.   I call this phenomenon a "penny from heaven" – in the United States, this usually appears out of nowhere as a penny face up in front of you with Abraham Lincoln's face.   They are able to do this, because they are able to manipulate and rearrange time and space to bring you a penny from the 5th Dimension into this 3rd Dimension.

As Frank Joseph writes, "... physicists understand that there are no fundamental differences between energy and matter, that the latter is but a subatomic variant, rearrangement, or re-composition of the former," Atlantis and the Coming Ice Age, p.33. Perhaps this is one reason why Angels and spirits in the higher dimensions can sometimes send you a "penny from heaven."

I have had this happen many, many times. For example, sometimes when I am driving long distances, I will stop at a rest stop, and when I return to my car, a "penny from heaven" will appear on the ground, in front of my driver's door. This is the spirits' way to let you know they are with you and helping and protecting you.   It is a good sign that should not be ignored. In other countries, depending of course on their currency, you could have a small yen coin in Japan, a pence coin in Britain, or a small Euro coin in Germany. When something happens like this, and there is no logical explanation in the 3rd Dimension for a penny or another coin appearing out of nowhere, the coin is usually sent from the higher dimensions.

For those who think that a penny appearing out of nowhere is just a "coincidence", as my friend Albert Einstein has told me many times, there is no such thing as coincidence in this Universe.   According to Professor Einstein, we live in a deterministic Universe where *"The good God does not play with dice."* [1] In the spiritual world, things often happen for a reason.

2. CLAIRAUDIENT OR CLAIRAUDIENCE

Spirits can also communicate with you with voices. This is called "clairaudient", or "the power to hear sounds said to exist beyond the reach of ordinary experience or capacity, as the voices of the dead." [2] "Clairaudience" comes from the French where "clair" means clear with audience to mean the "faculty of seeing mentally or what is audible."[3]

An example of clairaudience happens where you are talking to another friend on the phone, when you start receiving messages from the other side. The messages are from the 5th and higher dimensions, and they usually speak very rapidly because they are in a higher dimension and vibrating at a faster rate. For example, you may say something like "I think I should go shopping today", and then I will hear a voice quickly say, "you're right".   Or I will ask the person I am speaking with a question, and before the other person has a chance to answer, I will hear a voice say "yes". My Dad (who passed away 20 years ago), or my brother (who passed away over 40 years ago) will often come into a telephone conversation with messages. I can usually hear them very clearly. In addition to giving me audible messages, they will also sometimes hit one of the keys on my telephone to let me know they are listening, or to send a message.

3. CLAIRVOYANCE

Clairvoyance is the "ability to gain information about an object, person, location, or physical event through extrasensory perception" and or things through your pineal gland or "Third Eye". "Clairvoyant" is from the French clair meaning "clear" and voyance meaning "vision." [4] The pineal gland actually has some of the same cells which produce eyesight in your eyes. The gland is also part of the Third Eye Chakra, allowing you to "see" in your imagination and heart mind anywhere in the past, present, or future on this or other planets or dimensions.[5]

When the clairvoyance of the Pineal Gland is used to view events in the past, present, or future in other places, this is called "remote viewing" or time/astral travel as referenced in the first section.

4. DREAMS

Actually a dream is not a "dream" at all – it is actually real because when you dream, you travel into the 5th Dimension, or into another (and different) time line. There are many different timelines of reality, and a dream state in alpha can lead right into another time line of existence.

Often it is easiest for spirits to come through to you in the dream state when you are in alpha or theta state. There are three main levels of consciousness: (a) beta (when you are awake), (b) alpha (when you are either just waking up or just going to sleep), and (c) theta or deep sleep. It Is easiest to remember your dreams from when you are in the alpha state. And when you are sleeping, your subconscious will easily accept spirits because there will be no conscious blocks. Spirits and guardian Angels on the other side will often give you important messages in your dream state, so it is important to remember these dreams. One of the best ways to remember your dreams is to keep a journal next to your bed, so when you wake up early in the morning, you can write down your dreams.

For example, recently I drempt that I was in a city where I had just given a presentation. It was night but all the lights in the city were off. There was complete darkness everywhere. In the dream, I had to walk back to my hotel to get my suitcase. As I was walking, I realized that everyone around me thought it was "normal" for there to be darkness everywhere. But I had a hard time finding my way in the dark, and eventually just gave up. The message of this dream is that many people in many places around the world live in world of spiritual darkness where there is no light; they think it's "normal" to be in the dark without any light.

As another example, during the 1990s I was doing a lot of volunteer environmental work to save and protect endangered salmon runs in Washington State in the US. However, by 1995, I did not know whether I should continue. But one night, I did receive an answer from a crow who talked me for some time during a dream. I dreamt that a big, black crow was high up in a tree when he started talking to me – I can still see his beak moving. He said he represented Gaia or Mother Earth. He told me how important it was for me to continue my work saving salmon. So I continued my work and the Endangered Species Act petition that I had filed to protect salmon was approved –

Mother Earth was happy! Many other times I have visited with my Dad (who passed away in March 1999), and other Angels from my spirit family in the dream state.

5. SPIRITS IN STONE

Spirits reside in the 4th, 5th, and higher dimensions. They can move into objects like rocks in the 3rd dimension. For example, when I visited Machu Picchu in January 2018, I photographed an Ancient Inca spirit in one of the stones – see photo:

I had a previous life among the Ancient Inca, and have been in contact with my brothers among the Inca since my first trip to Machu Picchu in October 2017.

Ancient Inca spirits in seaside rocks south of Paracas, Peru

As another example, here is the face of a Lemurian in the rocks at the entrance to Telos and the Hollow Earth at Mt. Shasta:

Photos from Machu Picchu

Once you have identified what I call a "spirit rock", you can put your right hand on the rock (if you are right handed), or left handed (if you are left handed), and receive messages and energy from the spirit in the rock.

6. ANGELIC LIGHT FROM THE 5TH AND HIGHER DIMENSIONS

Using a smart phone or camera, you can actually photograph Angelic light and spirits coming in from the 5th and higher dimensions, as illustrated by the photographs below:

Angelic light with a magenta spirit orb

Picture of reddish spirit orbs and Angelic light from the Sun

Angelic Lights

Machu Picchu (left) and Mt. Shasta (right)

Moon light has feminine energy that is softer than the light from daylight sun.

SENDING AND RECEIVING MESSAGES AND ENERGY

We are all powerful energy beings. Our auras extend out nearly 55 feet; everything we touch or use we can leave an energy signature. You can send and receive energy and messages with your hands. Generally speaking, you receive energy and messages with your non-dominant hand, and send energy with your dominant hand. For example, if you are right handed, you would send messages with your right hand (or your dominant hand), and receive messages with your left hand (or vice versa if you are left handed).

Because people leave an energy signature on objects and material things, you can also pick up energy from these items and receive messages. For example, my foster mother Teri used to work for Seattle area police departments as a psychic helping to solve difficult child abduction cases. They would give her someone's photograph or toy or piece of clothing and ask her what had happened to the child. She would often be able to very accurately give them information by just holding the picture or object in her hand. However, as you can imagine, it was often very difficult work because many children were either abused or not living.

When you visit an ancient or sacred site, you can use your hands to receive messages and energy from the site. For example, if you are at Stonehenge in England, try putting your hand on the stones and see what kind of messages or energy you receive. You can also try this with the Pyramids at Giza in Egypt, at the rock entrances to Telos or the Hollow Earth at Mt. Shasta, or at any of a number of sacred sites like Machu Picchu in Peru. I am sure you will be amazed at the energies and messages you will receive!

When sending or receiving messages from the people of Telos and the Hollow Earth, and the Pleiadians, you can also use your hands to send and receive messages. For the people of Telos and the Hollow Earth, you can simply put both hands over your heart and send love and light to them – they usually appreciate your gesture and often respond. For the Pleiadians, you can just use your dominate hand to send love and light to them. They will appreciate your loving thoughts. If you are outside at night, Pleiadian ships generally have a rectangle shape with four or more lights around their perimeter. If you send them lots of love and light, and ask them to respond, they often will do a little aeronautic dance for you in the sky to let you know they hear you!

8. ANIMALS AS MESSENGERS

Animals can also often appear as spiritual messengers. As one example, in 1995, I was volunteering my time to protect salmon and other endangered species on the west coast of the United States. I was not getting paid to do the work; I did it because I felt like it had to be done. But there came a time when I was wondering whether I should stop and do other things. My answer to this question came one night when I dreamed of a large black crow perched in a tree. The crow started talking to me; he said he was talking on behalf of Mother Earth or Gaia, and she and all the wildlife of Earth wanted me to continue my work. So after that dream, I did, and was able to protect some endangered salmon species on the U.S. West Coast with Endangered Species Act petitions. Now if I ever have any questions regarding the environment, I can always meditate and visit my big black crow friend for advice!

As another example, in August 2013, I was traveling by bicycle and camping right on a beautiful beach on Lopez Island in the San Juan Islands of Washington State. When I woke up one morning, the first thing I saw was a fox who came to within a few feet of me, and then left. Right after the fox left an owl appeared in a nearby tree and just looked at me for the longest time. After the owl finally left, a deer and her fawns came by to say hi, and then left, followed by a bald Eagle who flew over and circled me.

Each animal brought a different message to me. Seeing a fox encourages you to take action in quick, swift moves through any obstacles and resistance. [6]

I received this message just before I started my radio program in Seattle, and the message I received from the fox was spot on, because I had to make up my mind about starting a spiritual radio show. In September 2013, I signed a contract with 1150 Am KKNW Radio in Bellevue/Seattle Washington to start my own radio show. When I met the program manager at the station, after meeting with him for 45 minutes, I immediately knew that I needed to start my program with his radio station – I signed a contract for the show within 45 minutes after we met.

Ever since then, the show has been very successful. I now have over 200 million listeners in over 100+ countries! The purpose of my program is to make this world a much better and happier place at www.outofthisworld1150.com.

The owl represents wisdom, good judgment, knowledge, and a change or transition in your life, which is what exactly happened to me in the fall of 2013.[7]

A deer represents serenity and a message not to be too hard on yourself. Thus, the spiritual message from seeing a deer is "to be yourself and continue along your path."[8]

Finally, a bald Eagle is "a symbol for great strength, leadership and vision."[9] All of these messages were very important for me back in the late summer/early autumn of 2013 when I was making many changes and facing many obstacles in starting a new spiritual path. The fox, the owl, the deer, and the bald Eagle all had messages for me. This brings up another important point – you have to pay attention to seemingly little things which can carry important and profound messages for you from the spirit world.

9. BUTTERFLIES AS MESSENGERS

The vibration frequencies of birds, cats and dogs, and butterflies are much higher than most humans, so spirits can easily come into them to visit you. For example, while in Peru on a trip to visit Machu Picchu in January 2018, I was walking on a trail to Machu Picchu when this beautiful butterfly landed on my arm, and stayed there for 15 or 20 minutes:

I had an Inca brother from a past life among the Ancient Incas in Peru. As I walked on this sacred trail to Machu Picchu, my Inca brother's spirit came into this butterfly and stayed with me. He was letting me know that he was with me.

10. MESSAGES FROM THE SASQUATCH AND
THE MERMAIDS

There are many different creatures on Earth, including Sasquatch and Mermaids. Sasquatch are benevolent multi-dimensional entities who shift between this 3rd Dimension and the 4th and 5th Dimensions. They were originally created by benevolent 5th Dimensional human Extraterrestrials some 300,000 years ago, in an effort to jump start a human population. The genes of these benevolent humans were hybridized with a now extinct and ancient Sloth; the Sloth become extinct 200,000 years ago but the Sasquatch are still here and are found on nearly every continent.

There are four subspecies of Sasquatch, including one group called the "Ancient Ones", which are just like humans, except they are covered with fine short hair. The other three groups are hairy and more animal like. If a Sasquatch mates with a human, the offspring are viable and there have been many historical instances of this happening.

When I visit Mt. Shasta in Northern California, I always see the Sasquatch. They sometimes appear at our campsites, shifting in and out of 3rd Density into the 4th and 5th Dimensions. Once when driving down the mountain at Mt. Shasta, a Sasquatch crossed right in front of my car, only to disappear into the woods after he crossed. At other times, they have taken food from our campsites at night; we have also seen their makeshift stick homes right next to our campsite (see picture).

Because they are multi-dimensional creatures which go from this 3rd Dimension into the 4th and 5th Dimensions, they sometimes can appear in rocks, as illustrated by this picture:

They are also very artistic. Next to our campsite on Mt. Shasta in October 2019, they made this beautiful heart shaped figure with moss and stones:

On another trip to Mt. Shasta in July 2018, the Sasquatch made a beautiful peace mandala for the world:

And around the seven trees of the peace mandala, there were seven pieces of polished rose quartz crystals. The Sasquatch said the crystals were from Telos in the Hollow Earth.

Sasquatch leave markers in the forest and other places to demarcate their areas by piling rocks up, as in the picture below from the Mt. Shasta area:

They also leave markers on rocks:

In September 2017, while camping at Mt. Shasta next to several entrances to Telos and the Hollow Earth, one of the people camping with me named Tami was given a miraculous healing by the Sasquatch. Tami had come from Minnesota to camp with our group on Mt. Shasta. She had arrived late at about 11 pm – after going to sleep, at about 2 am, the Sasquatch surrounded her van where she was sleeping, and asked her if she wanted a healing for her legs. Tami had crippled legs for the past 20 years and was unable to walk without a cane and/or wheelchair. Tami told them that she would very much like a healing.

So as soon as she said this, an Extraterrestrial craft from the Hollow Earth appeared over her van, and sent a beam of light to the top of her van. The van opened up and she was transported to the UFO from the Hollow Earth where she was given a new set of legs, and then placed back in her van. The next morning she woke up and was running around the campsite yelling "they healed me" over and over again. At first I thought she was on drugs, but when I talked to her, I realized she had experienced a miracle healing.

In addition to the Sasquatch, there are many pods of Mermaids and Mermen everywhere around the world. You can contact them by simply going to the ocean and putting your bare feet into the ocean water. Then after covering yourself with white light, meditate and ask the Merpeople to talk to you – and they will! They were created by the Atlanteans about 200,000 BC when the Atlanteans first came to the Earth to harvest seafood. They were a mix between the Atlanteans and dolphins. They are benevolent beings who also care deeply about us, and who want to help us with our Ascension into the 4th and 5th Dimensions. I myself live close to the Pacific Ocean, and have communicated with the Merpeople many, many times.

11. MESSAGES FROM NATURE DIVAS AND THE ELEMENTALS

In addition to the Mermaids and the Sasquatch, there is also a vast world of nature divas and what is called the "elementals". These are the plant spirits. When I visited a beautiful nature preserve in Costa Rica in 2017, I was walking along a trail through the tropical forest when green nature spirits hovering in the forest suddenly appeared. The nature spirits appear as small green winged Angels like entities in the picture below (see green natural spirit at the bottom of the picture):

At Findhorn in Scotland, "when Eileen & Peter Caddy and Dorothy Maclean came together in 1962 to seek divine guidance, they had no intention of growing a world-famous vegetable garden and starting a community, but that's exactly where their guidance led them." [10]

Peter Caddy, the founder of Findhorn, wrote that "man, the (nature) divas, and nature spirits are part of the same life force, creating together and because our thoughts and states of mind affected the garden, one of the most vital contributions we could make was the radiation we put into the soil while cultivating it and the plants while tending them." [11]

Findhorn represents the first time that people were "consciously working hand-in-hand with the spiritual aspects of the nature kingdoms,"[12] with phenomenal results! The plant and nature spirits taught them and their friends how to enrich the soil so plants could grow and thrive. With the advice and guidance of these amazing spirits, they were able to transform dozens of acres of sand dunes into one of the most productive and fascinating gardens in Europe.

This beautiful story of Findhorn illustrates several important lessons, namely, when you pay attention to the good advice of benevolent spirits and elementals in the higher dimensions, the manifestations of the good things in the higher dimensions will always reflect themselves in the 3rd Dimension. In addition, the other lesson of Findhorn is that we are powerful spiritual beings who create our own reality.

Dr. Masaru Emoto found if we send positive thoughts to a glass of water, the vibrations of the water would rise and when frozen, create beautiful water crystals. Conversely, if negative thoughts were sent to a glass of water, that ugly patterns would emerge. He also found that the most beautiful water crystals would form with the words of love and gratitude.

Dr. Emoto once did an experiment where he and 500 other people in Japan sent thoughts of love to a glass of water 10,000 miles away to an office in Los Angeles. Scientific photos of the water molecules before and after this experiment found that the positive love thoughts of these 500 people changed the water molecules in this glass of water in Los Angeles when frozen into beautiful crystals.

In another experiment, Dr. Emoto took a bottle of radioactive water from a nuclear plant in Japan, and wrote the words "love and gratitude" on the bottle and also pasted beautiful "love and gratitude" water crystals on the bottle. Within 48 hours, all the radiation in the bottle was completely gone! Water has memory and the higher vibrations of the words "love and gratitude" and crystals positively affected the water and raised its vibration, completely eliminating all the radiation.[13]

For areas polluted with radiation like the Fukushima nuclear reactors, or the radioactive waste tanks of Hanford in Eastern Washington in the USA, how difficult would it be to write the words "love and gratitude" on the nuclear tanks or nuclear waste tanks? It seems like a simple solution, but Dr. Emoto proved that it would work!

1 http://open-site.org/Science/Physics/Modern/Quantum_Mechanics/

2 https://www.dictionary.com/browse/clairaudient

3 The Concise Oxford Dictionary of Current English, c.1978. p.182

4 https://en.wikipedia.org/wiki/Clairvoyance

5 http://thelills.com/the-pineal-gland-and-third-eye-chakra/

6 https://www.spiritanimal.info/fox-spirit-animal/

7 https://trustedpsychicmediums.com/spirit-animals/owl-spirit-animal/

8 https://www.spirit-animals.com/deer-symbolism/

9 http://www.pure-spirit.com/more-animal-symbolism/629-eagle-symbolism

10 https://ecovillagebook.org/ecovillages/findhorn/

11 The Findhorn Garden Story. c.1975

12 Ibid., p.8. See also: https://www.ecovillagefindhorn.com/

13 Messages from the Masters, Ted Mahr, p.76-77

CHAPTER 26

CREATING YOUR REALITY

Findhorn and Dr. Emoto's findings brings us to another important point – we are powerful spiritual beings who create our reality, and we should be able to create love, abundance, and happiness. Thus, there are several different techniques which can bring you an abundance of health, wealth, and happiness.

The first technique I would recommend is to visualize health, wealth, or love or happiness for yourself in the future, and then take that positive energy of abundance, and bring it to you now -- visualize that you already have health, wealth, or love/happiness now.

1. FINDING AND/OR CREATING/ATTRACTING LOVE

If you want to attract love, you can do a very effective "love ceremony" with the following; (a) take a white sheet of paper and fold it into a triangle, so it forms a pocket, (b) put six red rose petals into the pocket, (c) then light a red candle, and (d) place a piece of hard red candy on top of your tongue – this will be the beautiful, sweet love that you will be receiving from your new sweetheart or soul mate. Then keep this love ceremony packet on you 24/7; you can put in your pocket or purse and put it underneath your pillow as you sleep. You can ask God and the Love Angels for a specific kind of person or with certain physical characteristics (for example, tall or short, etc.), but most of the time, I simply leave it up to God as to who I should meet. It is always good to be open and optimistic when you use this love prayer, because you don't know when you will meet your sweetheart or soulmate. But it is very effective and has worked for most people who have tried it, within one to four weeks!

2. CREATING WORLD PEACE

We are all powerful spiritual beings, and we can create world peace. For example, before he passed away in October 2014, Dr. Masaru Emoto of Japan was one of the world's most spiritual people. A few months before he passed on July 25th, 2014 from 3 pm to 4 pm Pacific Time, I interviewed Dr. Emoto and asked him if his experiments with water crystals could also help bring about world peace. He said yes that it should, so we spontaneously decided to do a meditation for world peace with him and about 30,000 listeners at the time who were listening to my show.

At that time, there was fighting between the Israelis and the Palestinians, so we spent about five minutes at about 3:30 pm that day on the show, asking everyone to pray and meditate for a 12 hour cease fire to exchange food and medical supplies for the wounded for both the Israelis and the Palestinians.

After the show ended at 4 pm, I drove to where I was staying at about 8:30 pm, and turned on CNN – just at that moment, there was a small red banner across the TV screen saying that the Palestinians and the Israelis had spontaneously agreed to a 12 hour cease fire to exchange food and medical supplies for the wounded for both the Israelis and the Palestinians. So our intention experiment worked!

According to one source, "In 1978, researchers discovered what they call the Maharishi Effect. They discovered it when a group meditation of 7,000 people took place and they all meditated with the intention of having a positive effect on the city. They did this for 3 weeks. The results of that group meditation transformed the city's crime rates, acts of violence, and death. There was an average reduction in all three by 16%; impressive!"[1]

During the Lemurian and Atlantean ages of Earth, the "soul practitioners of first Mu and then Atlantis engaged in mass-mediation sessions involving hundreds, thousands, and occasionally millions of participants. The psychic power generated from these single-minded assemblies went beyond anything experienced before or since. Levitation of otherwise immovable objects, psychokinesis, communal telepathy, remote viewing, metaphysical healing, the shifting of space and time, prophecy, inter-species communication, inter-dimensional travel ..." were all possible with mass mediation, [2]

Looking at from another way, "When You Change Yourself, You Can Change the World. You Are Pure Energy." [3]   Thus, I think Mahatma Gandhi was correct when he said that if you want to change the world, change yourself first – he said, "You must be the change that you wish to see in the world." [4]

3. BRINGING IN FINANCIAL ABUNDANCE

There are several ways to bring in financial abundance:
1.   You can write the number "8" on a piece of paper and put it in your wallet or purse, and this will attract money.
2.   You can carry a green stone in your pocket or purse and this will also attract money.
3.   You can use visualization to bring in financial abundance, by visualizing wealth coming in the future, and then drawing upon that energy and bringing it to you now.
4.   You can also use what is called a "Hado water machine" to change your vibration to attract money or even find love, and/or many other things. (Please see the following points)
All of these methods do work!

4. HEALING AND HEALTH ISSUES

(a). Hado water healing

Before he passed away in October 2014, Dr. Masaru Emoto found that everything is vibration or "Hado" in Japanese. He also realized that if you change your vibration, you can heal nearly any physical or spiritual condition, or bring money or love into your life. While he was alive, he used a special Hado machine to successfully treat over 10,000 people. He would program water to help heal people.

Once the water was programmed, people would just need to drink the water and they would be helped. His programmed water treatments are being carried on today by Michiko Hayashi with the Emoto Peace Project in Tokyo, Japan. If you would like a treatment, please email: hayashi@hado.com or visit www.emotopeaceproject.net.

(b). Healing ourselves

According to my friend Zorra in the Hollow Earth, we are all powerful spiritual beings, with the power to heal ourselves. He taught me a healing prayer to help people, and if you would like to try and heal yourself, please say this prayer several times a day:

"5, 4, 3, 2, 1,
I receive from the God/Goddess with me,
Healing for _____
(list what you would like to heal)

And I now feel much better and I am healed,
And I know it to be true".

You can also use this simple prayer to help you with almost anything, as long as you are sincere for the highest and best good.

(c) Mt. Shasta Miracle healings

Since 2015, I have been visiting Mt. Shasta, California. The mountain is one of the world's most spiritual places, containing many entrances to Telos and the Hollow Earth. Telos is an Ancient Lemurian civilization that has been beneath Mt. Shasta for about 12,500 years.

Mt. Shasta-ancient writings at entrances to Telos

Some places on Mt. Shasta have areas where there are ancient writings in the various entrances to Telos and the Hollow Earth from the Lemurians.

Many miracle healings do occur on the mountain from Adama and the Lemurians who live in the City of Telos beneath the mountain. For example, when I visited Mt. Shasta in October 2019, a woman who had many torn ligaments on her left foot was spontaneously healed after 30 minutes of prayer on the mountain.

And again in September 2018, my eyesight was spontaneously restored to 20/10 crystal clear eyesight from 20/50 blurry far sighted vision in my right eye – my eyesight was spontaneously healed by Adama, the high priest and spiritual guardian of Telos one night after camping on the mountain.

Other people have been healed of Lou Gehring's disease, fiber myalgia, and other health problems (including being given a new pair of legs for walking after being crippled for many years), after praying and asking for healings on the mountain.

I take a small group of people to Mt. Shasta every year. If you would like to visit Mt. Shasta with me, please feel free to email me at: outofthisworld1150@gmail.com.

In addition to Adama and Telos, Saint Germain and many other ascended masters will also visit and help people at Mt. Shasta. Saint Germain carries with him what is called a violet flame of sacred spiritual energy – it "is useful for those who desire to make all things new, and who wish to transcend from the present state of being."[5]

5. PAY ATTENTION TO SEEMINGLY LITTLE THINGS, AND GO WITH THE FLOW

Often, benevolent spirits will place obstacles in your path if you are going in a direction that could cause you harm. As one example, one time I was planning on going on a drive out to the ocean. I live about 1½ hours from the Pacific Ocean -- I love walking along the ocean beaches. However, on the day that I was going to drive out to the beach, my car would not start, and so I had to use another car.

When I drove this second car to the service station to get gas for the long drive, the gas pump malfunctioned and would not work, neither would another pump that I tried. So it finally dawned up me that I was not supposed to go to the ocean that day. As things turned out, the weather was really stormy and rainy, and there were power outages. So it would was a good thing that I did not go on my trip that day.

When you contact benevolent Angels and spirits on the other side, and you receive negative information, please remember you have a choice. I tell people when I do readings that if you do this, these things will likely happen. But if you do something else, something else will happen and you can change the future.

Thus, when dealing with negative information or possible events, remember this is a planet of free will, and we are all powerful spiritual beings. We can all make good choices to avoid any negative event, and by doing so, we can make this world a much better and happier place.

6. WHAT TO DO WITH NEGATIVE MESSAGES

Negative messages bring up another important point, i.e., when you open up the door to the other side, you never know what will come through. As a psychic, you owe an ethical and spiritual duty to relay information to the people that you are doing a reading, without bias and not knowingly substitute or slant the information you receive. Of course, we are all human, and we all have our own unique perspectives on the world. However, the information you receive should be given in a neutral way as much as possible to people. When you receive negative information, you should always give people choices, because this is a free will planet.

If you give people negative information without giving them choices, you can unwittingly cause them harm. Medical doctors sometimes do this unknowingly when they tell a patient for example that they have cancer and "only have six months to live", because there might be health alternatives which could really help them (if only they were given a choice of various treatments). The mind is a very powerful thing and if you receive a message and then tell them that someone is "going to die within six months", you can help cause the very thing that you are trying to prevent.

So when you receive negative information, it is always best to try and give options to people. For example, in July 1999 when I was living in Olympia, Washington, I was going to drive some five hours to visit my foster mother in Spokane, Washington. However she called me and told me to not to drive over to see her on that day – she told me to delay my trip by one day. So I had a choice – I could take her advice and delay my trip, or drive over as planned that day.

I took her advice, and drove over the next day to Spokane to see her. However, on the next day when I left, there was a front page story in the local paper about how there had been a terrific car accident on the freeway the day before on the day that I was going to leave – it I hadn't taken her advice, I would have likely been in the middle of that accident (and been harmed).

7, USE PSYCHIC POWERS ONLY FOR GOOD

There are people who misuse their psychic powers for their own selfish gain, or to harm others. If you misuse your powers in this way, you may have success for a short time, but in the long term, the spirits will stop you. This is because it is an unwritten spiritual law that you are only supposed to use spiritual gifts for good purposes.

If someone abuses this power (like Sylvia Browne who started charging $5,000 for her readings, and/or "Q" who assaulted women in his sessions) God and the Angels will take away your spiritual gifts if you abuse them.

8. START A SPIRITUAL GROUP WITH A LOCAL

PSYCHIC

It is good to have support when you are developing skills to talk to the other side. I have a spiritual mentoring program where I teach people how to talk to the other side. People are welcome to contact me if you would like any help and support at: outofthisworld1150@gmail.com.

You can also start a support group with a Psychic in your area and talk about psychic and spiritual things. I was fortunate to have the help and support of my foster mom who taught me how to talk to the other side. With her help, I have been able to experience thousands of life reviews, allowing me to advance many hundreds of spiritual lifetimes, or approximately 4000 years.

9. GET REST AFTER DOING READINGS

Talking to the other side takes energy, and if you do many readings, you will need to take some rest, preferably in nature. If you don't rest, you could actually shorten your life. Edgar Casey was a famous psychic who helped many, many people with medical readings which often cured them. He would do many, many readings to help as many people as possible. However, he was warned by the spirits that if he did not cut down and take some rest from all the readings he did, he would shorten his life and die early. He did not heed the warning and died before his time.

In addition, during this time of Ascension where the vibrations of Earth are rising higher and higher, people will tire easily, and so it is important to get the rest you need. If possible, take a nap or sleep in if you are tired, your body is adjusting to the new rising frequencies of the 5th Dimension.

Of equal importance is to drink plenty of water, and remain well hydrated. We all originally came from Lyra where we were water beings. So water is very important for our bodies and our souls.

---

1   https://www.higherperspectives.com/science-has-proven-that-group-meditation-literally-changes-the-world-1406180384.html?fbclid=IwAR3gPUpbeBo-UQkJc7ww7RvcJZ2E-hbo5VUPQcEitgpiQK5jc52IqR5rdrc

2 Frank Joseph, Atlantis and the Coming Ice Age, Bear and Co. c.2015. p.152)

3 https://projectyourself.com/blogs/news/when-you-change-yourself-you-can-change-the-world-you-are-pure-energy?fbclid=IwAR1xPujaXBdzcGKrS-R0Bo1VfoLItoHKKuuQ_7uSdrS9qP_Zxje3MtOGy5w

4 https://www.brainyquote.com/quotes/mahatma_gandhi_109075

5 "Who is St. Germain?" https://www.crystalwings.com/AI_who_is_saint_germain

PART 3

CONCLUSION

CHAPTER 27

THE END OF KARMA

Many of us who are here on Earth now had lives in Atlantis, where some of us made wrong choices resulting in the destruction of that civilization. George Bush Sr. was present in Atlantis and helped destroy that civilization with his bad choices for war and conflict. Although President Bush could have made the right choices for a beautiful loving and peaceful planet, he repeated his mistakes again with his push for a "New World Order" during his first term as President during the late 1980s and early 1990s, where humanity would be controlled and destroyed again.

Psychics in Japan call the U.S. "Atlantis 2.0" because the government here is making the same mistakes that Atlantis did 12,500 years ago. In fact, toward the end of the Atlantean civilization, the government back then required everyone to take a vaccine that ended up killing and disabling many people. One of the reasons why Atlantis was destroyed is because they started mixing human and other animal genes together to create half human, half animal beings like Mermaids and Mermen. Other mixed beings were part dog and part amphibian. Today some children being born of vaxxed parents are also being part frog and part amphibian. Other babies being born of vaxxed parents today have black eyes, indicating they do not have any souls. (This is different from children who have black eyes from sexual abuse.)

However, playing with human DNA was against Galactic law and God's law during the Atlantean times, and it is still against God's law and Galactic law today. So, these dangerous and spiritually hazardous games with human DNA will eventually be forced to end, just like it was 12,500 years ago. God and the Galactics will not allow this same mistake to happen again.

Humanity on this planet has tried six other times to ascend into the higher dimensions but failed each time. During the Atlantean times, many light workers for example tried to stop the madness toward destruction but failed. However, we will not fail now, because we are getting help from the Supreme Being as well as Galactic and Pleiadian help. There are also more light workers who are aware who are requesting assistance from the higher realms. Our Ascension has already been delayed too long due to the interference of negative entities; it is time now for humanity to ascend for those who are ready to evolve into the higher dimensions.

The Earth is like a big school where we can learn many different lessons. As part of that learning experience, we are all souls inhabiting a human body. Many of us had lived through Atlantis but have come back now to learn from our mistakes to make better choices during this lifetime for a better and happier planet.

Karma was instituted as an experiment on this Earth by the Supreme Being. To have karma, there needed to be a dichotomy between light and dark; between good and evil. Evil was instituted as an experiment here as one way to get people to choose the light over the dark; to make good decisions instead of bad; to be service to others rather than service to self, and to make decisions which helped push them toward (instead of away from) God. The theory was that if people were punished for their bad decisions, that they would hopefully learn from their mistakes and choose good over evil.

Many believe when people do bad things to each other, that it will bring back 10 times of negative karma to the perpetrator. However, this karma system has not worked out very well to propel humanity to higher spiritual levels and so it is now ending.

This change was confirmed in 2012 when there was a meeting of the Dali Lama and other Native American spiritual leaders in the Southwest United States – the most important conclusion from that meeting was evil as an experiment was ending here on planet Earth. For years, I wondered what that meant, but now I know and would like to share this very important and profound message with everyone.

The end of evil as an experiment on Earth will see negativity and darkness replaced with love and light. The wars and conflict are now being replaced with peace and harmony. One of the first steps toward this beautiful spiritual transformation is the realization that we all have God within us. We are all interrelated and are one. All negative entities will soon be leaving the planet because the vibrations of the planet will shift so high into the 4th and then 5th Dimensions that negative people, and negative spirits and entities will not be able to survive here anymore. This includes negative Extraterrestrials like the Reptilians and their slave species, the Greys – within the next year or two, these negative entities will be completely gone.

This also fits in with the destiny of Earth to become a truly beautiful, loving, and harmonious place where all wars and conflict will become a thing of the past. The destiny of Mother Earth is to ascend. Some say she has already ascended, and humanity now is just trying to catch up.

I have also been told by my spirit friends the hardest planet to effect positive change on has been this one. The rest of the planets in this solar system have already started to ascend. As a rising tide lifts all boats, all of the planets in this solar system are now in the process of ascending – Earth has been the laggard planet. But now all that is changing, and we will soon shift into the 4th Dimension, and then the 5th.

A TIME OF TRUTH!

This is also a time of truth – and the truth will set you free! With the Ascension of planet Earth into the higher dimensions, truth will become even more important now than it has ever been in the past because everyone will be able to read each others minds through telepathy. As a result, no one will be able to lie to anyone else anymore. This will be like a new skill for many people. It will take some time and practice to embrace and develop it, but it will a wonderful part of our New World. Once people ascend into the higher Dimensions, they will just know how to behave in a more loving way and with a transparency that they have never been experienced before now.

In April 2014, I had a wonderful astrologist from New York City named Susan Miller on my Out of this World Radio show.[1] Susan said during her interview that this was a time of truth for Earth and humanity, those things which are true will become self evident and those things which are false would show themselves to be false and fall by the wayside.

In the 5th Dimension, there is only truth, and everything is transparent. The main way to communicate will be telepathic. Thus, no one will be able to hide anything from anyone.

When this happens, politicians and political leaders will soon realize that they cannot lie or hide anything from the people they serve. Married couples, and partners and sweethearts will be able to read each others minds, and not hide anything from each other.

The Lemurian City of Telos is 5th Dimensional, and advanced humans there communicate telepathically. They also cannot hide anything from anyone because of this transparency.

This is an exciting time because we will be able to communicate with each other without any language (and without any misunderstandings). In the 5th Dimension, we will experience what I call "pure heart/mind communication" where we will also realize that we are all one. Once we realize we are all one, we will not wish to hurt anyone else. If we do we are actually hurting ourselves. This will lead to the end of war and conflict as we know it today, the Earth will truly become a place of peace and harmony.

From my conversations with Nostradamus about this new harmony, there will no longer be any need for large centralized governments. People will just know how to treat each other with love, harmony and respect, as with animals today. A flock of birds or other animals do not need their own animal "government" to regulate their behavior – they just know to treat each other with love and respect. All animals know about God.

In like fashion, with conflict among the peoples of the Earth gone, government size will shrink. There will of course be a need for a "government" but this new government will only act as an interface with other Extraterrestrial civilizations.

With these changes, the nature of many current educational and medical institutions will completely change. For example, instead of forcing children and young adults to all become the same, the system will encourage individual freedom to learn. Far less emphasis will be placed on control, and instead, actual individual learning will be encouraged and supported. For healthcare, cures for cancer and other diseases which have been suppressed for years will become freely available as the Rockefeller/Big Pharma medical mafia will be dismantled and fall by the wayside. Ironically, this process will be accelerated as many doctors and nurses will die off from the vaccines. Gradually an entirely new system of true health care and cures (instead of sick care) for all diseases will emerge. This change will coincide with our lifespans increasing to 300, 400, and more years as we all evolve toward becoming immortal.

THE WORLD IS SPIRITUALLY IMBALANCED

AND NEEDS TO BE CORRECTED

As in Atlantis, in the past, our world was spiritually imbalanced. But the good news is that we are slowly correcting this as we stand up for the truth and want to make this planet a much better and happier place. In the past, the planet was imbalanced in favor of negative logical materialistic energies and power which focused on war and disharmony. However, this is all changing now, where we are rapidly moving toward the integration of the divine masculine and the divine feminine.

In advanced human societies on other planets outside of Earth, human societies are much more balanced between male and female energies. This balance helps us to find the truth answers to our questions and will greatly help accelerate our development.

Plato wrote in two dialogues (Timeous and Kittitas), "human societies begin to self-destruct when their citizens no longer honor organic relationships between the spiritual and the material spheres of existence."[2] This happens when an "imbalance in one, sets up a deteriorating resonance in the other."[3] This is how Atlantis was destroyed and how today's society may also be destroyed if we do not correct this imbalance between the spiritual and material spheres. According to Plato, an "imbalance in one ... sets up a deteriorating resonance in the other."[4]

Such a bond is unseen until the consequences of cosmic disharmony reveal themselves in physical destruction."[3] Atlantis destroyed itself by becoming too materialistically oriented; the civilization embarked on a worldwide quest to dominate and enslave the world, and played with nuclear and crystalline based weapons which eventually destroyed much of the Earth 12,500 years ago.

According to Professor Einstein, when humanity started playing with nuclear technology at Hiroshima and Nagasaki in 1945 with the needless murder of hundreds of thousands of innocent people, we were making the same mistakes we did during the Atlantean times, which lead to our destruction. According to one article, "... the stark truth is that the U.S. atomic bombings of Japan did not save the lives of any U.S. military service members as Japan had been attempting to surrender for several months prior to the atomic bombings. Following the U.S. capture of Marianas Island and the commencement of the B-29 firebombing campaign against Japan's largest cities in July 1944, Emperor Hirohito ordered the Japanese government to negotiate Japan's surrender in the belief that his refusal to do so would result in the United States exterminating the Japanese." [5]

As Professor Albert Einstein wisely said after he helped create the atomic bomb, "I made one great mistake in my life, when I signed the letter to Franklin D. Roosevelt recommending that atom bombs be made."[6] He added, "The release of atom power has changed everything except our way of thinking... the solution to this problem lies in the heart of mankind. If only I had known, I should have become a watchmaker."[7]

LOVE IS THE ANSWER

According to Professor Einstein (and many others), love is the most important and powerful force in the Universe. In 1955, he wrote the following letter to his daughter Lieserl. On a "Bomb of Love" for the world. He wrote:

... "When I proposed the theory of relativity, very few understood me, and what I will reveal now to transmit to mankind will also collide with the misunderstanding and prejudice in the world.

I ask you to guard the letters as long as necessary, years, decades, until society is advanced enough to accept what I will explain below.

There is an extremely powerful force that, so far, science has not found a formal explanation to. It is a force that includes and governs all others, and is even behind any phenomenon operating in the universe and has not yet been identified by us.

This universal force is LOVE.
When scientists looked for a unified theory of the universe they
forgot the most powerful unseen force.

   Love is Light, that enlightens those who give and receive it.
Love is gravity, because it makes some people feel attracted to
others.

   Love is power, because it multiplies the best we have, and allows
humanity not to be extinguished in their blind selfishness. Love un-
folds and reveals.

   For love we live and die. Love is God and God is Love.

   This force explains everything and gives meaning to life. This is the
variable that we have ignored for too long, maybe because we are
afraid of love because it is the only energy in the universe that man
has not learned to drive at will.

   To give visibility to love, I made a simple substitution in my most
famous equation.

   If instead of E = mc2, we accept that the energy to heal the world
can be obtained through love multiplied by the speed of light
squared, we arrive at the conclusion that love is the most powerful
force there is, because it has no limits.

After the failure of humanity in the use and control of the other
forces of the universe that have turned against us, it is urgent that
we nourish ourselves with another kind of energy...

   If we want our species to survive, if we are to find meaning in life,
if we want to save the world and every sentient being that inhabits
it, love is the one and only answer.

Perhaps we are not yet ready to make a bomb of love, a device
powerful enough to entirely destroy the hate, selfishness and greed
that devastate the planet."[8]

I think both the Beatles and Albert Einstein were right – all we need is love to solve the world's problems! We do not need to fight anymore, but instead to "live as one", as John Lennon wisely noted in his famous song, "Imagine":

"Imagine there's no countries   *Living life in peace*
It isn't hard to do   *You may say I'm a dreamer*
Nothing to kill or die for   *But I'm not the only one*
And no religion too   *I hope someday you'll join us*
Imagine all the people   *And the world will be as one"*[9]

The key to solving our problems is love, as Professor Einstein and Jesus and the Beatles have all wisely noted. However, the Cabal/Deep State are trying to stop our Ascension by having the so called "vaccines" attack our hearts with myocarditis and shut down our pineal gland and all our chakras including our heart chakra so we cannot connect with God through our intuition.

Intuition from our pineal gland is from the higher realms and is always for our higher good. Intuition and love connect us all with the Supreme Being, and so it is essential for us to maintain this connection so we can make the right decisions to make this world a better and happier place. I think the greatest teaching of God and Jesus is love. All the great teachers (including Albert Einstein, Jesus, the Beatles, and many others) have all said that the most powerful and important force in the Universe is love. Thus, I think the Beatles were right when they sang "All We Need is Love."

---

1 http://outofthisworld1150.com/guests/susan-miller/ for April 11, 2014

2 Frank Joseph, "Atlantis and the Coming Ice Age", p.12.

3 Ibid., p.12.

4 Ibid., p.12

5   https://nationalinterest.org/blog/buzz/atomic-bombings-japan-did-not-produce-its-surrender-204074(August 9th, 2022)

6 https://wisdomquotes.com/albert-einstein-quotes/

7 Ibid.

8 https://jeffreylouismartinez.blogspot.com/2016/02/a-love-bomb-letter-from-albert-einstein.html

9 John Lennon, Imagine Lyrics, at:

https://duckduckgo.com/?q=john+lennon+song+world+will+live+as+one&t=chromentp&atb=v314-1&ia=web&iax=lyrics

CHAPTER 28

UPDATED MESSAGES FROM THE GREAT MASTERS: THE CORONA VIRUS

Ever since the time of Atlantis, there has been a battle going on between good and evil – between the forces of light and the forces of dark, and negative and positive energies. Many souls who were present 12,500 years ago have reincarnated now. They have the opportunity to make new choices for a better and happier planet, rather than make the same mistakes they made thousands of years ago, and this time destroy the planet. Fortunately, many souls now on the Earth realize and recognize what the negative forces are doing and have chosen to make this world a better place.

1. Albert Einstein

Recently, Albert Einstein and many other great spirits came to me and gave some important messages. Professor Einstein said, "We went through the same drama when Atlantis ended. We failed back then but will win now. You and I (Ted) worked in a laboratory together there. Our objective was to increase capacity for energy for the Atlantean civilization. However, a small group of military leaders took our work and twisted it for their own ends to control the world and ended up destroying themselves. We are back in the same position now, but the light will win this time. Thank you for working together to bring forth all these messages. You and many other light workers are making a real difference in this ascension and all of us on the other side are applauding your efforts.

We realize this is not easy, but we thank you for being of service to others and not service to self. This is the hardest planet in the universe on which to make any positive changes but you're doing it and you will be successful. We are all with you 1000 percent. So don't ever feel like you will lose this battle as long as you keep trying and know that the white light is always stronger than the dark."

Professor Einstein then quoted Shakespeare with this famous quote, "All the world's a stage, and all the men and women merely players: they have their exits and their entrances; and one man in his time plays many parts, his acts being seven ages."[1]

Corona Virus

With Shakespeare's famous quote in mind, Professor Einstein said the Corona virus is a replay of the same tug of war between the positive and negative forces which has been going on at least since Atlantis, with many of the same spirits who did not learn their lesson 12,500 years ago with the fall of Atlantis.

Because "all power tends to corrupt and absolute power tends to corrupt absolutely."[2] and "those who fail to learn the lessons of history are doomed to repeat it." [3] Negative forces are trying once again to stop our Ascension to the 5th Dimension.

With the sudden appearance of the virus in late 2019/early 2020, negative entities are once again trying to pervert the planet Earth into one vast police state, where the U.S. Constitution is abolished. They wish to deny the people of the U.S. and indeed the whole world the freedoms we all deserve.

They want us all to be totally controlled by the state, micro-chipped and vaccinated. "Immunity passports" have been put forth as a requirement for people to have before they drive, travel, even buy food, etc. [4]

As in Atlantis 12,500 years ago, this is nothing more than a blatant attempt to control and subjugate humanity into slave like conditions. However, we are all very powerful spiritual beings meant to create a much better and happier world, and their negative efforts to enslave humanity will fail.

The Corona virus was created as a bio-weapon by a Bill Gates controlled company called "Pirbright."[5] And his wife Melinda Gates said Gates had been "preparing for years for the virus"[6] with a Rockefeller sponsored plan called Operation Lockstep that was created in 2010.[7]

As part of this so called "Operation Lockstep", Bill Gates spent 17 trillion Dollars and Warren Buffet spent another 30 trillion Dollars creating the Corona virus, to reduce the population of Earth by 95 percent. However, special forces units from the Galactic Alliance came in during the fall of 2019 and eviscerated the worse parts of the virus so people would not die. Although this was successful in reducing the deadliness of the virus, the Cabal controlled mass media in the U.S. and around the world filled the world with fear about the "virus" and how we all needed to be "vaccinated". As Adolf Hitler found during World War II, if you tell a big lie loud enough and long enough, people will believe it – even if essentially means suicide.

During this plandemic/scamdemic in 2020 and 2021, although less than half the number of people who normally die each year from the flu have died from the Corona (Covid-19) virus, much of the U.S. (and the world) was locked down for months causing massive unemployment and the closing of many small businesses. For example, in 2018, 118,000 people died from the flu in the U.S., many more than the Covid-19 but there was nothing in the controlled U.S. mass media on any flu deaths. And you must ask why a shutdown is there now in many parts of the world when there no pandemic. Negative elements tried to kill as many people as possible with the virus. Now that the virus has failed, they are trying to instill fear into as many people as possible. But their efforts will fail. We have a bright and beautiful future ahead of all of us – we just have to make the right choices and stand up to the governments in the United States, Europe, Australia and elsewhere who all want to kill and/or harm us.

The virus and the masks and so called "social distancing" were all based upon lies and propaganda. For example, "In the decade preceding the pandemic, the mean IQ score on standardized tests for children aged between three months and three years of age hovered around 100, but for children born during the pandemic that number tumbled to 78" (or over a 22 percent decline), with the use of masks, isolation, and social distancing as primary factors.[8] Even though there were no scientific or medical reasons why masks and social distancing work, they were forced upon many adults and children worldwide population by many governments.

Then when the vaccine rollouts started in late 2019/early 2020, governments around the world urged everyone to get the shots, even though the vaccines were rushed through in record time with almost no testing. Unfortunately, the vaccines proved deadly in the U.S. and in other countries as death rates and illnesses skyrocketed from the shot programs.[9]

There were apparently three levels of death programmed into the shots where people would die in three stages: (a) within 10 to 14 days of heart attacks, (b) within 5 or 6 months from heart attacks and/or cancer and other diseases, and (c) within 1 ½ to 2 years from Mad Cow disease and/or HIV/AIDS.[10] This information was obtained from the actual computers at Pfizer, Johnson and Johnson, and Moderna and proves that these companies knowingly killed many people with their so called "vaccines."

For babies born to parents to who had taken the shot, most babies died, and others were born without eyes – they were called "black eyed babies" without souls and without any emotions. [11]

These black-eyed babies were actually a product of the mRNA technology in the shots which mixed human DNA with alien DNA from the negative Reptilians and Greys. Thus, babies born with black eyes (or without pupils) were not actually "human" anymore. [12]

In response to a court order, Pfizer was forced to release disease and death data from their so-called vaccines in 2022.[13] Their own data listed over 100 different diseases in their vaccines, from cancers to HIV/AIDS to heart attacks and strokes, with many dying from taking the shots. In fact, there was ABSOLUTELY NOTHING GOOD in their Covid vaccines.

Thus, what appeared at first as a solution to the so called "virus" was a genocidal weapon to kill humanity and reduce population. Big Pharma targeted "Red States" which voted for Trump in the 2020 election. Much higher death rates were reported from all Red States like Kentucky vs. Blue States like California which had a 90 percent lower death rate from the vaccines. So, it appears that Big Pharma was trying to wipe out conservative Americans with their deadly shots. Some Red states even had deaths up to 16 times higher than many Blue Democratic States![14] This is nothing but genocide!

In 1917, "… Rudolf Steiner Foresaw a Vaccine That Would 'Drive All Inclination Toward Spirituality Out of People's

Souls," [15] Mr. Steiner wrote: ". . . a way will finally be found to vaccinate bodies so that these bodies will not allow the inclination toward spiritual ideas to develop, and all their lives people will believe only in the physical world they perceive with the senses."

In 1917, he wrote about a time (i.e., now) when greedy, materialistic medical doctors would inject children and adults with a vaccine that would remove their spirituality.[16] In fact, the so called "vaccines" all disable and/or destroy a person's pineal gland, so they cannot have any intuition or the ability to talk to God. The vaccines also destroy a peoples' chakras, so they lose the ability to feel and give love or compassion or feel any other emotions. After five or six months, people become automatons without any emotions, and their souls leave their bodies, with many dying from HIV/AIDS (among other diseases).

Research in France has confirmed this finding. For example,[17] this healer writes: "What happens in the energy bodies and especially in your soul after the "vaccination"? Experience of a therapist who has been working for many years with energy, with energy healing, with the subtle bodies, but above all with the radiation of light and the frequency of the vibration of the heart, the seat of our soul, to achieve deep contact with the higher self. "I was having a session with a person who had received the first and second doses of the vaccine. I had already energetically treated that person, but I didn't know they had taken the vaccine. When I started treatment, I noticed immediately the change, very heavy energy emanating from his / her subtle bodies. The scariest thing was when I was working on the heart chakra, I connected with her soul: it was detached from the physical body, it had no contact and it was, as if it was floating in a state of total confusion: a damage to the consciousness that loses contact with the physical body, i.e., with our biological machine, there is no longer any communication between them.

During the treatment, this soul told me that it no longer felt the body and had the impression of floating in a deep discomfort ..."

I have also spoken to Mr. Steiner on the other side. He tells me he was writing about this time in human history when he wrote this essay. He says we are currently in a deep spiritual war of good vs. evil, of light vs. dark, of freedom to slavery. He tried to warn humanity of this time when he wrote there would be a time when greedy, materialistic doctors would use "vaccines" to separate people's souls from their bodies, so they would lose any connection to spirituality and God.

However, for those who have taken the shots, or who have been harmed by "shedding", there are inexpensive remedies available. Shedding happens when people take the shots, because when they take the shots, they become biological weapons factories spreading the deadly Spike protein everywhere they go. If left untreated, shedding can harm and kill people. This was all planned by Bill Gates and Warren Buffet to reduce the world's population. However, you can heal yourself if you believe in God and want to live, because there are remedies available. (Please see Remedies Sheet in Appendix A.)

We have a bright and beautiful future ahead of all of us – we just have to be strong and optimistic and make the right choices. All eyes of many civilizations are watching what choices we make, and benevolent ETs and many Angels are also helping us as much as they can. For example, the Pleiadians have been beaming tremendous positive energy and vibrations to planet Earth for several years now. They tell me that their positive energy and high positive energies are helping people heal from the vaccines and helping them make better choices to create a better and happier planet. So, we are getting help! I would recommend everyone reading this book to please send lots of love and light to the Galactic Alliance and to our beautiful Pleiadian friends for their wonderful help and support!

2. Benjamin Franklin

According to Ben Franklin, after the Ascension we will be able to teleport ourselves and we will not have a need for vehicles or planes as we do now. We will be able to go anywhere on the planet and energy portals will be available to take us to the other Universes and other dimensions.

He says that the Pleiadians are 444 light years from earth and are able to travel to earth from their home in 6 hours using these portals. The Reptilians have always wanted the use of these portals, but they will not be allowed to gain control of Earth to use them.

Mr. Franklin also says that the Annunaki genetically modified humanity, shutting down many strands of our DNA. However, with the Ascension, 22 stands of our DNA will be reactivated, giving us amazing powers of telepathy and other powers. In some people, these abilities are starting to open up already.

He also says that the Cabal and Bill Gates have used vaccines to shut us and our children down, but this will not work, because our children will have an amazing future full of love and light. He says that this virus is a last-ditch attempt by the negative entities to stop our spiritual evolution. We will have a much better world, and this tyranny will then end.

3. President Dwight D. Eisenhower

President Dwight D. Eisenhower says this is the beginning of the New Earth, and the end of the old. Nothing will be seen as the same as you are seeing now. This is the evolution or spiritual path that has been denied to us for the past 80 years.

He says it is a very exciting time for the Earth. Things in the 5th Dimension will appear alive and we will understand the connectedness of everything from the smallest to us. This is an evolution or a spiritual path that has been denied to us for the past 70 or 80 years. It's going to happen now because people are waking up and it is our destiny.

All of the great spirits and Angels are helping, including President Kennedy, Nostradamus, Mahatma Gandhi, Dr. Masaru Emoto, Archangel Michael, Archangel Gabriel, and Archangel Raphael – they say, "We are all helping you achieve your destiny."

President Eisenhower says he made a big mistaken when he agreed to the illegal Treaty of Merida in March 1954, which allowed the Reptilians to abduct and "study" us humans, in exchange for some of their advanced technology to fight the Soviet Union. "I regret this decision, but the Ascension will help with my karmic debts and the mistakes I made when I was President during the 1950s. In this new world, there will no longer be any karma to create because we will be living without polarity in a space of love. It will be a beautiful New World."

4. Archangel Michael

Archangel Michael is a powerful spiritual warrior. He says you are being protected and helped more than you realize. He says, "I'm here to help you though this Ascension, each and every one of you – all 7.8 billion of you. You have all sped up the timeline so you will be ascending within the next 2 to 3 years much faster than even we thought possible a few years ago.

Your light-work and advancement has far exceeded our expectations and we all (including all Ascended Masters and all benevolent beings of this Universe) congratulate you on your success! You have many other universes and other planets which are in Earth's space which are watching this transformation, and many are helping/assisting in it.

This is an enormous gift for all of us to watch and be a part of it. No mistake – all of those attempting to prevent this Ascension will fail, and be removed from this planet."

Archangel Michael is carrying his big golden staff and putting in the ground, saying "I claim this benevolent place for the betterment of all universes." All universes will learn and grow from this planet.

He is also showing a crystal grid and another grid is being placed on top of it – it's a grid for the 5th Dimension, and it's being activated. Soon everyone will be able to heal themselves and Mother Gaia will be healed and the planet as a whole will be healed. He is protecting all of us.

There will be a new understanding, and everything will appear different. The beauty in everything will be realized. Creativity will flow (grow) and this new beauty will be seen in all different aspects of creativity. For example, buildings and other structures will all have a different universal beauty that everyone will see. This planet is truly picturesque when seen from above. Just wait for our gifts to be opened and we will all experience it.

5. Archangel Gabriel

Archangel Gabriel says, "At this great time of creativity, there is an understanding and a feeling of being connected. Humanity will not only realize that we all are connected to all including the plants, animals and non- living entities in this universe, but it will all be revealed to us.

We will have an all knowing and feel the energy and healing from everything. You will feel it in your heart and soul. This immense understanding will lead to much new creativity and tremendous new inventions.

Remember we are all Gods and Goddesses with the same capabilities of the Supreme Being. You can and will make this planet a paradise. This is the start of a truly wondrous age for humanity. You will succeed and there is no turning back now."

6. Nostradamus

Nostradamus says: "Welcome to the Age of Aquarius. The planet has finally made it. All predictions have come true. We've all waited a long time for this moment in your planet's history. The potential is enormous as to what will happen next. All of us here would love to be there now to be a witness to this magnificent event in the history of the universe. Everything on your planet is about to change in large ways, and I'm here to tell you that telepathy will be your way of communicating, at teleportation will be your main way of transport."

He adds: "You are being brought into a space that all of you have been before. This change is so beautiful for you, in a quantum reality in a brighter and better place. Sit back and enjoy this change for 1000s of years! Prepare to see life as a journey and yours has just begun. The animals will be ascending too and they will also shift into this higher dimension, bringing them new abilities to speak to us telepathically."

"We are genetic royalty with the history of 22 different races in our DNA. Contained within our genetic structure are 22 strands of DNA all of which are starting to wake up. Once we ascend into the 5th Dimension, these strands will help us become even more powerful than we are now."

He adds, "Service to self will change to service to others, and money will no longer be an obsession. The perception of value will change from money to spiritual relationships when we realize the potential we have and we use that potential to create a realized planet – and that will be the source of our power and strength. There will be no need for money, there will be such love and giving in your hearts to others."

Nostradamus adds, "The countries of the world will have spiritual leaders and live in peace and harmony. Humanity will become very strong with all the gifts we were born with. We have been endowed with more gifts than most other entities in the universe. We will have a loving heart and wish to give love and support to each other."

In addition, he states: "Vaccines and the 5G cellular system will be used to shut us down and stop our Ascension. They will be unsuccessful. Also, the Corona virus and vaccines are the last try of the Cabal to stop humanity's Ascension. It will get much better after this is all over."

There are many amazing inventions happening right now on the planet, for example, with the new technology which allows desalinization of large volumes of water. Water sustains all life. Water is very important; it gives life to everyone on the planet. There will be free energy devices which can be used to operate all types of automobiles and aircraft as well as heat homes. This will eliminate our dependency on fossil fuels.

He continues, "We will lose our desires to eat meat for we will truly understand our connectedness with Earth's animals. We will marvel at growing our own food, and our bodies and taste for food will change. The world will only grow in this quantum reality to sustain us. It's going to be a beautiful New World, with pristine waters, no sickness, clean air, no garbage (spiritual or physical), a time of truth, and a delight to be of service to others. This is a time I've spoken about before and it is upon us now". He said, "There will be no more predictions regarding our future, what is meant to be will be love and grace. Our future will be what we make of it."

He also said, "You are coming into a time when all things as you know them will change. Change sounds scary to some but this change will be so beautiful for you. You will be existing/living in a quantum reality with unlimited potential. Your world will be a brighter and better place. Open the flood gates for this energy is flooding in. Sit back and enjoy it. Living in the new quantum state will last for thousands of years. Your planet will become a super model for other civilizations across the galaxies. Prepare to see life through the Supreme Creator's eyes and be in true wonderment. Life is a journey and yours has just begun."

7. Chief Running Bear

Chief Running Bear of the Cherokee also gave me this message: "Hello my son, it is so good to talk to you finally. We have watched you for years and are so glad you have reclaimed your Indian heritage. (My Great, Great Grandmother was full blooded Cherokee from the Trail of Tears – I am 1/16th Cherokee Indian and an enrolled member of the United Cherokee Nation of Georgia and Missouri.)

In our time when I was alive in your earth time, we lived in harmony with the planet for many 1000's of years. When white man came everything was thrown out of balance and everyone lost the harmony. (The Chief is showing me the Prophecy Rock on the Hopi Reservation – the rock showed two paths of humanity: the first path was of destruction, and the second path was of harmony and peace. See picture in Chapter 32.) I have good news; you were on a path of destruction but now are on a path of peace and harmony.

Follow your heart mind in everything you do and know you are receiving a lot of help for your spiritual journey; the best is yet to come and we will be with you in spirit to help you create this new golden age.

Listen to your heart and mind in everything you do and try to raise consciousness around you in all ways so as many people will come along with you on this ascension – President Kennedy then came in and said, "leave no neighbor behind". Our great-great grandmothers are with us now and will be with us helping us in our lives now. *Nieodmienny.* (Thank you in Cherokee, a specific expression of gratitude).

8. Chief Seattle

After Chief Running Bear, Chief Seattle came in and said that he and his people understood about living in peace and harmony with the land. During his time in 1854, Chief Seattle met with Washington Governor Stevens at his home in Seattle. Stevens was militaristic and wanted to take Native land.

During that meeting, Chief Seattle said: "Your religion was written on tables of stone by the iron finger of an angry God, lest you might forget it. The red man could never remember nor comprehend it. Our religion is the traditions of our ancestors, the dreams of our old men, given them by the great Spirit, and the visions of our sachems, and is written in the hearts of our people. Your dead cease to love you and the homes of their nativity as soon as they pass the portals of the tomb. They wander far off beyond the stars, are soon forgotten, and never return. Our dead never forget the beautiful world that gave them being. They still love its winding rivers, its great mountains and its sequestered vales, and they ever yearn in tenderest affection over the lonely-hearted living and often return to visit and comfort them". The Native Americans with Chief Seattle were in harmony with the planet and with other people, both those living and those who had passed away. However, Governor Stevens represented very different values.

However, Chief Seattle said this is a very different time now, where the Ascension will help people understand that everyone (Native Americans and others) are all our brothers and sisters. He said, "it is the time to stand tall and accept all for all its beauty. Peace will truly serve the planet and love will reign now because we are all one."

9. Mother Mary

Mother Mary then said: "Love to Humanity. We are all beaming with light at this monumental time. The foundation has been set and it is truly glorious. We are grateful to all the ascended masters that chose to return to earth and assist during this time. We are pouring our love out to you all.

Time as you know it will cease to exist in the new vibration. Many there are holding space in the 5th Dimension of love for the planet now. Waves of energy are being sent to your planet and many are feeling it. Take notice of the beauty around you and remain in a state of love, grace, and gratitude. Remain steadfast and you shall succeed."

10. Mary Magdalene

After Mother Mary, Mary Magdalene said: "Bless you all for hearing my message. Remain in love, connecting this love through your heart and mind. You are gifts to humanity, realize those gifts now and share them helping others. We are all one, connected, intertwined and it is the time for this truth to envelop your beings.

During meditation ask for the mystery school teachings and spiritual gifts to be brought forward now so each of you would have the complete understanding of who you truly are. Feel the love of the Supreme Creator within you, around you and in others. Your potential is limitless. Your potential is limitless. Realize this and know I am always with you."

11. Admiral Halisourus

Admiral Halisourus of the Pleiadians then came in and gave this message: "The entire universe is watching you now for you are the best and most exciting show around. We owe a karmic responsibility to you.

52,000 years ago, we had a long civil war among our peoples and both of us left the Pleiades to come to Earth. One reason is that we were escaping conflict among the Pleiadians. Also, during this time, there was a nuclear war and 60 million of our Pleiadian people were killed. We were able to escape in large mother ships. You and other light workers were on those mother ships that came to Earth as we agreed to come to Earth to help with the Ascension of this developing planer. .

After that time, we left you alone for 10,000 years. We shouldn't have abdicated our responsibilities to help you. We chose to help although the Universe has the prime directive of leaving planets alone, of non-interference to allow their own evolution. However, with Earth, it is a special situation because we incurred a karmic debt to you all by not helping you earlier.

The Reptilians stepped in at this point and took over your planet earth. They cannot be allowed to succeed because the planet is slated for Ascension. Also, after the Reptilians and Cabal have murdered thousands of people, we are here to help you with the Ascension until you succeed. We will join you on the planet after the Ascension in physical form. We are proud of your spiritual progress and are here to help. Call on us anytime during this crucial time."

12. Jesus

Jesus loves us all so much, and he came in with this beautiful message: "This is the end of times as you know it. Those that choose to go thru the planet's Ascension will be entering into a beautiful reality full of opportunities and spiritual advancement.

I would ask humanity to ready themselves by forgiving one another including families, neighbors, and those that you perceive or judged to have done wrong. Also forgive yourselves. Help one another and be of service to them.

This is the time to reflect and let go of the old in preparation for the new. Unwanted negativity across the planet will be released and removed as you release, forgive, and heal making way for the surging of a higher vibration.

Love one another and yourself. Fill you heart space with unconditional love and allow the overflow to spread out across the planet helping all those people that may need it now. Anything is possible with Love. I will always be here helping mankind and never left you. Ask and you will receive."

13. President John F. Kennedy

President Kennedy then quoted his famous inaugural speech and said: "My fellow Americans, ask not what this country can do for you but what you can do for your country." He said the Earth is shifting from service to self to service to others. This is now the watershed moment in history. We have waited tens of thousands of years for the new world, and it is here now." He adds, "This is an exciting moment in history. We are all where we need to be and holding space for others. We all have a purpose for where we are now."

Importantly, President Kennedy said, "Don't seek out the shifted (higher dimensional) places on the Earth but let your love and energy flow to the other parts of the planet which need help in raising their vibrations. To ascend, we must bring all with us – we should leave no one behind.

We can't walk forward alone. We must walk forward together for we are all connected. Leave no neighbor behind. We are all holding the space for people wherever we are. We all have a purpose being where we are. You can't move forward without your neighbor." He adds that "A lot of people will come to Mt. Shasta (or Sedona) and expect instant ascension. But ascension comes from within, and the hard work required for internal advancement. Humanity should focus on letting go of their past trauma and heal them to make this transition. We all need to be holding space for the Ascension of the planet."

President Kennedy says the world today is experiencing a great spiritual awakening. President Kennedy tells me that the Earth today is full of pockets of white light, and soon the entire Earth will become one big ball of white light.

In a series of books called "Conversations with Nostradamus", published from 1986 to 1989, Dolores Cannon channeled Nostradamus. In these books Nostradamus predicted that the Earth would shift into the 5th Dimension by 2038. However, since that time, the spiritual evolution of the planet has greatly accelerated. Parts of Mother Earth will start shifting into the 5th Dimension by early 2025 (or sooner). It has greatly sped up because the majority of us are making the right choices to make this world a much better and happier place!

1 115Brainy Quote at: https://www.brainyquote.com/quotes/william_shakespeare_166828

2 Lord Action, from: https://duckduckgo.com/
q=lord+acton+quote+power+corrupts&t=h_&iar=images&iax=images&ia=images

3https://duckduckgo.com/
?q=those+who+ignore+history+Lord+Action&t=h_&iar=images&iax=images&ia=images&iai=https%3A%2F%2Ftaras
itser.files.wordpress.com%2F2016%2F06%2Fthose-who-ignore-history.png%3Fw%3D550%26h%3D178)

4 "Beware of Antibody-based COVID-19 'Immunity Passports' – Dozens of tests with dubious accuracy have
flooded the U.S., thanks to a move by the FDA that loosened restrictions", from: https://
blogs.scientificamerican.com/observations/beware-of-antibody-based-covid-19-immunity-passports/

5 "Bill Gates funded the PIRBRIGHT institute, which owns the patent on coronavirus" at: https://
www.newstarget.com/2020-01-27-bill-gates-funded-pirbright-institute-owns-coronavirus-patent.html

6 "Bill Gates Melinda reveals billionaire "prepared for years" for coronavirus pandemic", from:
https://www.express.co.uk/news/world/1269765/bill-gates-wife-melinda-gates-coronavirus-pandemic-who-Donald-
trump?fbclid=IwAR2p3BQXC-CP36tKSRuCYlEfb8MiN80x26VoJHO_sLX2aVSqDLTuoMm2ZVE

7 "Citizens willingly gave up some of their sovereignty — and their privacy — to more paternalistic states in exchange
for greater safety and stability" (P18) "A world of tighter top-down government control and more authoritarian
leadership, with limited innovation and growing citizen pushback"

The Rockefeller Fndn., Scenarios for the Future of Technology and International Development (p. 18) From: https://
envirowatchrangitikei.wordpress.com/2020/05/24/under-the-guise-of-a-pandemic-we-will-create-a-prison-state-the-
rockefeller-foundations-documented-plan-for-martial-law-operation-lockstep/

8 https://www.theguardian.com/world/2021/aug/12/children-born-during-pandemic-have-lower-iqs-us-study-finds

9: 76,253 Dead 6,033,218 Injured Recorded in Europe and USA Following COVID Vaccines with 4,358 Fetal Deaths in
U.S.", July 23, 2022 3:30 pm, https://healthimpactnews.com/2022/76253-dead-6033218-injured-recorded-in-europe-and-
usa-following-covid-vaccines-with-4358-fetal-deaths-in-u-s/

10 https://www.howbadismybatch.com/states.html

11 https://voh.church/resources/black-eyed-babies-born-to-vaccinated-parents_237817/

12 https://www.ournewearthnews.com/2021/10/06/a-new-hybrid-is-born-70-million-black-eyed-covid-babies-born-
every-year-latest-reasonable-estimate-covid-plandemic-suddenly-changing-human-mating-rituals-and-reproduction-
after-millions-of-ye/

13 https://www.globalresearch.ca/bombshell-document-dump-pfizer-vaccine-data/5763397

14 https://www.howbadismybatch.com/states.html

15 https://www.wakingtimes.com/in-1917-rudolf-steiner-foresaw-a-vaccine-that-would-drive-all-inclination-toward-
spirituality-out-of-peoples-souls/

16 z'Fall of the Spirits of Darkness" (See: https://rudolfsteinerquotes.wordpress.com/tag/vaccine/

17 "A message from France - the experiences of a French energetic healer: Natalie Schaevers, [03/23/2021 at 8:39 pm]" at:
https://www.reddit.com/r/conspiracy/comments/mvpjd7/what_happens_energetically_after_the_covid/

CHAPTER 29

"BE THE CHANGE THAT YOU WANT TO SEE IN THE WORLD"

As Mahatma Gandhi has said, "Be the change that you want to see in the world."[1] He also said, "The day the power of love overrules the love of power, the world will know peace", and "The future depends on what you do today."[2]

We are all powerful spiritual beings. In fact, we are all "Gods" and "Goddesses", with a spark of God within each of us. We all have amazing attributes, the ability to heal ourselves and perform miracles. With practice and dedication, we can go into other dimensions, contact Angels and benevolent spirits, as well as Extraterrestrial life. And we can create a much better and happier planet.

We perceive objects in this 3rd Dimension to be "solid", but in reality, they are anything but solid because our reality is 99.9 percent space. This has been proven by many physicists, and Nobel Peace Prize winning researchers, including Niels Bohr – see: "When You Change Yourself, You Can Change the World. You are pure energy."[3]

"We and everything around us is energy. When you realize your true nature and perceive yourself as a spiritual being the barricades around you will begin to fade. The best way to understand the information above is through meditation and self-contemplation."[4]

In addition, at each frequency, "Our body produces vibrations. When you maintain your frequency at a high level, you are in a positive state of mind, and negativity can't influence you. However, if you are stressed, depressed or fearful, you have low and slow vibration, which will allow the negative energy to influence you."[5]   Thus, it is important to remain positive and upbeat.

Benjamin Franklin says in the new 5th Dimension, thoughts will become very important. For example, when you build a new house in this new spiritual world, people will recognize and use these new higher frequencies to create new homes in their minds. Because it will be a time of cooperation and harmony and service to others, people will help each other.

---

1 https://www.goalcast.com/2017/03/20/top-20-inspiring-mahatma-gandhi-quotes/

2 Ibid. (Emphasis supplied)

3 https://projectyourself.com/blogs/news/when-you-change-yourself-you-can-change-the-world-you-are-pure-energy?fbclid=IwAR1xPujaXBdzcGKrS-RoBo1VfoLItoHKKuuQ_7uSdrS9qP_Zxje3MtOGy5w

4 Ibid.

5 Ibid

CHAPTER 30

HUMANITY'S BRIGHT, BEAUTIFUL FUTURE - WE ARE ALL ONE

President John F. Kennedy has told me that the Earth is becoming a beautiful bright ball of higher spiritual light. There are some dark areas, but soon the entire planet will be a big, bright ball of pure white light as the entire planet shifts into the 4th and then 5th Dimension. We will realize that we are all one. We will realize we all have the spark of God within us, President Kennedy says that all conflict and wars will cease. When we hurt each other, we only hurt ourselves. We are all connected.

As this happens, we will all realize that we are all one with God or the Creator, with love and service to others as the highest goals which we should attain.

JFK says that we are not only all one with each other, but also with the plants and animals of Earth as well. Native Americans knew and understood this point very well. For example:[1]

(a) "All plants are our brothers and sisters. They talk to us and if we listen, we can hear them". – Arapaho.

(b) "When we show our respect for other living things, they respond with respect for us". – Arapaho

(c) "We will be known forever by the tracks we leave". – Dakota

(d) "Man's law changes with his understanding of man. Only the laws of the spirit remain always the same". – Crow

(e) "There is no death, only a change of worlds". – Duwamish

(f) "Life is not separate from death. It only looks that way". – Blackfoot

(g) "Treat the earth well: it was not given to you by your parents, it was loaned to you by your children. We do not inherit the Earth from our Ancestors; we borrow it from our Children" – Tribe Unknown

(h) "When a man moves away from nature his heart becomes hard". – Lakota

(I) "We are made from Mother Earth and we go back to Mother Earth. – Shenandoah

(j) "It is no longer good enough to cry peace, we must act peace, live peace and live in peace". – Shenandoah

(k) "Regard Heaven as your father, Earth as your Mother and all things as your Brothers and Sisters". – Tribe Unknown

Native Americans lived for many thousands of years in harmony and peace on this planet. They provide a wonderful model of how we can also live in harmony and peace as we ascend into the higher dimensions.

However, for beings who do not resonant with this new higher frequency, they will not be allowed to stay any longer on Earth. This is because Mother Earth is tired of being abused, polluted, and destroyed by a small group of people who only care about themselves. She says that this is part of the old Earth that will not be allowed to continue anymore on this planet.

For those who do not want to evolve, there is another Earth like planet that has been created on the other side of the Solar System (in the same orbital path as this Earth) in the lower Third Dimension. This lower dimensional Earth like planet has been created for those souls who refuse to wake up, or who just do not want to evolve into the higher dimensions. For these individuals, they will be exiled to this other planet for at least one Mayan Katun cycle, or 25,800 years, where they will be given another opportunity for ascension. Beings like Adolf Hitler, George Bush Sr., and John McCain are already all there now and I wish them well. I hope they make better choices this time!

There are some dark areas on Earth, but soon the entire planet will be a big, bright ball of pure white light as the entire planet shifts into the 4th and then 5th Dimension. We will realize that we are all one. We will realize we all have the spark of God within us, President Kennedy says that all conflict and wars will cease. When we hurt each other, we only hurt ourselves. We are all connected.

Native Americans had Ten Commandments which people would do well to follow today:[2]

1. Treat the Earth and all that dwell therein with respect
2. Remain close to the Great Spirit
3. Show great respect for your fellow beings
4. Work together for the benefit of all Mankind
5. Give assistance and kindness wherever needed
6. Do what you know to be right
7. Look after the well-being of Mind and Body
8. Dedicate a share of your efforts to the greater Good
9. Be truthful and honest at all times
10. Take full responsibility for your actions

1,2 Compiled by Kathy Weiser-Alexander, updated April 2020 https://www.legendsofamerica.com/na-proverbs/

CHAPTER 31

THE ANIMAL KINGDOM ALREADY REALIZES WE ARE ALL ONE

The oneness of humanity is also being realized by the animal kingdom: The realization that we are all one is also reaching and transforming the animal kingdom. More and more, animals are cooperating and engaging with other animals. For example, there are stories now of how a possum is "pulling ticks of a deer's face."[1]   Or how a dolphin is mothering a baby whale[2] Or instead of cats and dogs fighting, they are now friends:[3]

When we realize we are all one, we will stop eating meat, and recognize that we are not only all one with each other (regardless of race, creed, or color), but also the animal kingdom.

This may have already started because on November 25, 2019, U.S. President Trump signed a new federal law into effect where cruelty to animals is now a federal crime.[4]

The "Preventing Animal Cruelty and Torture Act (PACT) is the new law that "bans the intentional crushing, burning, drowning, suffocating, impalement or other serious harm to living non-human mammals, birds, reptiles, or amphibians."[5]

Most importantly, when we all learn how to become telepathic with other people, we will also become telepathic with other animals (and plants) as well. We will be able to not only talk to our pet cats and dogs, but we will also be able to talk to nearly any animal or plant like trees. It will be a truly enlightening experience for everyone who ascends into the higher dimensions.

---

1   https://www.sunnyskyz.com/blog/2945/Trail-Cam-Captures-Opossum-Pulling-Ticks-Off-A-Deer-s-Face?fbclid=IwAR07ZelyUc38LSwfSpZbKQU9ikfB_0Pv-EutBgeHUmDoOOL3zyX2Ww8lazA

2 Dolphin adopts a baby whale in 'astonishing' first known case" at https://www.independent.co.uk/news/science/dolphin-adopts-whale-bottlenose-melon-headed-calf-french-polynesia-a9029276.html

3 https://www.buzzfeed.com/alivelez/lets-take-a-cue-from-cats-and-dogs

4 https://www.npr.org/2019/11/25/782842651/trump-signs-law-making-cruelty-to-animals-a-federal-crime

5 Ibid.

CHAPTER 32

HOPI PROPHECIES FOR THE NEW WORLD – WE HAVE A CHOICE

On December 12, 1992, a Hopi spiritual leader named Banyacya of the Wolf, Fox and Coyote Clan addressed the United Nations. He said the "traditional Hopi follow the spiritual path that was given to us by Massau'u the Great Spirit. We made a sacred covenant to follow his life plan at all times, which includes the responsibility of taking care of this land and life for his divine purpose …. Our goals are not to gain political control, monetary wealth or military power, but rather to pray and to promote the welfare of all living beings and to preserve the world in a natural way."[1]

There is a famous rock called "Prophecy Rock" located on Hopi land in Arizona. The rock has five boxes along two lines – the two lines represent two paths civilization can take.

The top line is a zig-zag line that ends suddenly in the first box; the bottom line is a line that continues in a straight line around the rock, as illustrated by this picture:

According to Banyacya in his 1992 address to the United Nations,

"The creator made the first world in perfect balance where humans spoke one language, but humans turned away from moral and spiritual principles. They misused their spiritual powers for selfish purposes. They did not follow nature's rules. Eventually the world was destroyed by sinking of land and separation of land by what you would call major earthquakes. Only a handful survived.

Then this handful of peaceful people came into the second world. They repeated their mistakes, and the world was destroyed by freezing, which you call the great Ice Age.

The few survivors entered the third world. That world lasted a long time, and as in previous worlds, the people spoke one language. The people invented many machines and conveniences of high technology, some of which have not yet been seen in this age. They even had spiritual powers that they used for good. They gradually turned away from natural laws and pursued only material things and finally only gambled while they ridiculed spiritual principles. No one stopped them from this course, and the world was destroyed by the great flood that many nations still recall in their ancient history or in their religions.

The Elders said again only small groups escaped and came to this fourth world where we now live. Our world is in terrible shape again even though the Great Spirit gave us different languages and sent us to four corners of the world and told us to take care of the Earth ..."

We are now entering the fifth box of civilization on the Prophecy Rock. Will we follow the zig-zag line of materialism and end civilization?

Or will we follow the straight line of spiritual principles and create a beautiful, harmonious world free of war and conflict in balance with nature and Mother Earth? I think most people today will chose the latter.

As Professor Albert Einstein notes, the world today is spiritually imbalanced, but through the work of majority of us, we are creating a much better and happier planet. We are evolving to the point where it will be "normal" for people to talk to Angels and benevolent spirits and other beings (including Extraterrestrials) on the other side. People will need guidance and I sincerely hope this book will provide some needed direction and inspiration for people to talk to their guides and

Angels. There is a whole new world now opening up and we have a beautiful and bright future ahead of us all!

---

1 https://www.fwii.net/profiles/blogs/hopi-message-to-the-

united?fbclid=IwAR2hs_wMIHAP_pnspcoeasw4tYBbQFz2YuJJmzzv1y2pNxG9BhzunonggZo

CONCLUSION: LEARNING TO TALK TO THE OTHER SIDE IS A SERIOUS COMMITMENT AND YOU CAN DO IT!

Everyone can learn how to talk to the other side. However, as with everything, it requires patience, hard work, and an open and positive attitude. When you open yourself to the other side, you always want to protect yourself, and to be prepared for any message that comes through. Once you have prepared yourself to contact the other side you always want to protect yourself, and to be prepared for any message that comes through.

Thoughts are things on the other side. Because of this, you must have to pay attention to all of your thoughts as you communicate with Angels and spirits on the other side, as well as benevolent Extraterrestrials. In the higher dimensions beyond this 3rd Dimension, Angels, spirits, and benevolent beings all communicate in thought. And to prepare for communication, it is always a good idea to be in a good mood and not under the influence of drugs or alcohol. Many times is it a good idea to be in nature where Gaia (or the Earth) can give you energy and facilitate talking to Angels and spirits. We came from the Earth and are all part of the Earth. Gaia or Mother Earth will help us if we ask for help.

Many of us came from other parts of the Universe to be part of this Ascension now. It is an exciting time to be here on Earth because no planet has ever shifted so quickly from 3rd Density to 4th Density in a matter of just a few years, followed by an ascension into the 5th Dimension. This is because it normally can take up to several hundred thousand years for a planet to shift from 3rd Density (or 3rd Dimension) to 4th, and then onto 5th.

The Earth is also unique because it is a 3rd Dimensional water planet ruled by our free will. Very few planets meet all three criteria and no planet in the history of this Universe has ever accelerated so quickly and so fast from one dimension to another. And despite many different obstacles from the Deep State and the Cabal, as well as their Reptilian and Grey ET masters, we are ascending! God and Gaia (or Mother Earth) are all helping us achieve this amazing and profound transformation and it is truly an honor to be here at this moment in the history of this beautiful planet.

We are all powerful spiritual beings meant to create a beautiful and harmonious planet. The destiny of planet Earth is to ascend to the higher dimensions. We would have already ascended into the 5th Dimension in the 1960s had President Kennedy not been assassinated, but he and Jackie are still our President and First Lady on the other side. He and Jackie are both still helping to bring peace, harmony, and joy to the world.

As part of this ascension process, we will be able to talk to the other side. Soon it will be "normal" to talk to people who have passed on, as well as to plants and animals, as well as the people of Telos and the Hollow Earth. And when we talk to those who have passed on, this will all give us so much joy to realize there really no such thing as death. There is only a change in energy. Since we are all souls inhabiting bodies to learn lessons in this big school called Earth, we are all immortal, with the spark of God or the Supreme Being within all of us.

Many people will need guidance in learning this new skill to talk to the other side. And the book is meant as a guidebook on how to talk to Angels and benevolent spirits and beings on the other side, as the world learns to "live as one".

In the words of John Lennon, "You may say I'm a dreamer, but I'm not the only one. I hope someday you'll join us. And the world will live as one." [1T]

There are negative governments and negative entities like the Reptilians and the Greys who want to stop the Ascension process, but we have reached the point where there is no turning back. If a government tells you to get the vaccine, refuse! If they tell you to drink fluoridated water, refuse! If they try and lock down your business, refuse! We have much more power than they do, and we all are powerful spiritual beings meant to live free and happy! The lesson of the scamdemic was that we should all stand up for our rights.

As Delores Cannon said many years ago about Karma and Human Evolution, there is a split now happening on the Earth between those who want to live in a beautiful peaceful and positive world, and those who do not.[2] We are all powerful beings, and we all can create the kind of world we want to live in.

So let us create a beautiful planet where people are free and happy and there is no more war and no more conflict! Let's get rid of the Deep State and the Cabal, and all the politicians who lie to us and who don't care about the people they are supposed to serve. The choice is ours and all of us should stand up for our rights and make the right choices, so we all become free and happy!

I have nearly 30 years' experience in talking to the other side, and I teach people how to talk to the other side, along with Angels and benevolent Extraterrestrials.

If interested, please sign up for my mentoring program at outofthisworldreadings.com
or email me at outofthisworld1150@gmail.com or outofthisworldradio@protonmail.com. We have a bright and future ahead of us! If we all work together, I know we can create a beautiful and happy world!

---

1 https://www.passiton.com/inspirational-quotes/7460-you-may-say-im-a-dreamer-but-im-not-the-only

2 https://www.facebook.com/watch/?v=716750436181048&extid=NS-UNK-UNK-UNK-AN_GK0T-GK1C&ref=sharing

APPENDIX A

Remedies Sheet for Shedding and the Vaxxed

To guard against the shedding and to help with the effects of the vaccine, I would recommend the following home remedies from various medical doctors and health care professionals:

(a) Pine needle tea,
https://beforeitsnews.com/health/2021/05/huge-is-pine-needle-tea-the-answer-to-covid-vaccine-shedding-suramin-shikimic-acid-science-mike-adams-must-video-3039419.html

(b) See: Dr. Judy Mikovitz – ANTIDOTE TO THE VACCINE https://projectcamelotportal.com/2021/04/29/antidote-or-what/

(c) HCQ (Hydrocholorquine) -- can make with three grapefruits and three lemons. (If you cannot get grapefruits, you can also use limes or oranges.) Take the rinds from the two fruits and then cover with water about two inches higher than the rinds in a metal pot. Simmer for two or three hours, then let cool down and sweeten with honey to taste and drink. It will really help! I would add a crushed up Zinc tablet to the drink – this will boost the effectiveness of the HCQ drink.

(c-1) Tonic or Quinine Water (with a Zinc tablet) – This contains HCQ and you can simply buy it at any grocery store or market. Drink one or two bottles of this every day and it will help prevent getting shedded – this will also help with the negative effects of the shots.
(d) Zinc, Vitamin C and E.

(e) Invermectin.
(f) Fennel Tea – very effective in helping with the shedding and the vaccines.

You can also say this prayer from the Hollow Earth:

(a) Count down the numbers from 10 to 1. After you say each number, breathe in and out.
(b) Then snap your fingers.
(c) Then say: I ask and command God to completely heal me from the vaccine (and/or the shedding), and I know it to be true.
(d) Then snap your fingers.
(e) Then say: I am now completely healed and I know it to be true.
(e) Then snap your fingers.

In addition, you could say this 10th Dimensional healing sequence of numbers: The numbers should be written on your arm with your finger. There is a different sequence of numbers for each vaccine: (Thanks to Linda Jollo, LMT)

Pfizer:
6 9 281 692 5 8 9 69 02 1425

Moderna:
2 3 5 6 10 1213 69 59 00 29 8 13

Johnson and Johnson:
1 1 6 9 32 78 3 5 96 143 248 90

Keep writing these numbers on your arm several times a day until you feel better.

High vibrational water.
For example, you can make 4th Phase water with a Nubian pyramid – drink the water for a week to destroy all nanobots and everything in the vaccine.

Dr. Lee Merritt, M.D. also has many recommendations on her website at: www.themedicalrebel.com

Finally, if you don't wish to comply with the vaccines and mask mandates, please see this link: https://fightthemandates.godaddysites.com/ as well as: https://childrenshealthdefense.org/

APPENDIX B

KENNEDY SHOT DEAD

Gunned Down During Drive Through Dallas

DALLAS (Texas), November 22.

PRESIDENT KENNEDY was assassinated to-day. The President was shot as he drove through this Texas city in an open car. The Governor of Texas (Mr John Connally) was seriously wounded. The President died at 7 a.m. Saturday, New Zealand time. After the burst of gun-fire cut down the President, he was rushed to Parkland Hospital, where blood transfusions were given.

Priests were summoned to his bedside for the last rites of the Roman Catholic Church. The President was cradled in his wife's arms immediately after the shooting. Mrs Kennedy, who was unhurt, sobbed, "Oh, no," as the President slumped back with a shot in his head.

The assassination took place near a three-highway intersection close to the business area of the city. Within seconds of the shooting, Mr Kennedy slumped over in the back seat of the car, face down. Mr Connally lay on the floor of the rear seat.

Arrested Man Lived in Russia

DALLAS (Texas), November 22.

POLICE have arrested a man employed at the building where a rifle was found after President Kennedy's assassination, British United Press reported.

ENLIGHTENED AND FIRM ACTION WAS HIS MARK

LONDON, November 22.

JOHN FITZGERALD KENNEDY, son of a former United States Ambassador to Britain, was the first Roman Catholic to become President of the United States. Educated at Harvard University and the London School of Economics, he served with distinction as a naval lieutenant during World War II in the Pacific. He was discharged on medical grounds from the United States Navy in 1946 and worked as a newspaper reporter.

Copy of the 1963 newspaper from New Zealand printed the day before Kennedy's assassination.

Made in the USA
Monee, IL
30 April 2023

32594918R40089